Professional Automotive Paint Refinishing TechBook

Steve Rendle

The Haynes Manual for Professional Automotive Paint Refinishing

ISBN **1 85960 741 1**

British Library Cataloguing in Publication Data
A catalogue record for this book is available from the British Library

ABCDE
FGHIJ
KLMNO
PQRST

Printed by **J H Haynes & Co Ltd, Sparkford, Nr Yeovil, Somerset BA22 7JJ, England**

Haynes Publishing
Sparkford, Nr Yeovil, Somerset BA22 7JJ, England

Haynes North America, Inc
861 Lawrence Drive, Newbury Park, California 91320, USA

Editions Haynes
Tour Aurore – IBC, 18 Place des Reflets
92975 Paris La Defense 2 Cedex, France

Haynes Publishing Nordiska AB
Box 1504, 751 45 UPPSALA, Sweden

Contents

Introduction

The aim of this Manual is to provide the inexperienced automotive paint refinisher with a source of information and advice, which can be used in conjunction with practical training to develop his or her skills to a professional level. The materials, equipment and processes described in this TechBook assume that the reader is working in a 'body shop' environment with access to professional equipment. Details of DIY refinishing are not included. Other than the filling and repair of small scratches and dents, details of bodywork repair (panel beating, repair of major body damage and renewal of panels) are not included in this TechBook, as this is considered to be a separate subject in its own right.

Chapters 1 to 7 deal with important background theory, including health and safety considerations, legislation on the handling of refinishing materials, and details of the equipment and materials in common use. Chapters 8 to 16 provide full details of the various individual procedures used when carrying out professional refinishing work, whilst Chapter 17 draws on the information given in earlier Chapters to give step-by-step examples of two of the most common refinishing operations. Chapter 18 provides a guide to fault diagnosis.

Acknowledgements

We would like to thank all those people at Sparkford and elsewhere who helped in the production of this TechBook.

Special thanks are due to Tetrosyl Limited Refinishing Division for the provision of information, and for the use of the workshop facilities and vehicles appearing in the photographic sequences. Thanks are due to Alan Bailey, Training Centre Manager at Tetrosyl for his help and encouragement during the writing of this book; to Paul Scargill of Redhouse Engineering Limited, Taunton, for his goodwill and for the supply of air compressor information; to Ian Bunker of DeVilbiss Industrial Coating Equipment, for the supply of spray gun information; to Steve Vallis of Partco, for the supply of technical information; and to Paul Tanswell who took the photographs appearing in this book.

We take great pride in the accuracy of information given in this manual, but no liability can be accepted by the authors or publishers for loss, damage or injury caused by any errors in, or omissions from the information given.

Chapter 1

An introduction to professional automotive paint refinishing

Contents

Introduction

Automotive paint refinishing is an industry in its own right. As long as people continue to drive vehicles, there will be plenty of business for refinishing specialists, repairing the damage which occurs due to scrapes and accidents, corrosion, and even genuine wear and tear. There is also, of course, work which involves spraying new body panels and shells for restoration projects and modified vehicles, and customised spraying work (although this is a specialist subject which is beyond the scope of this book).

Before explaining the subject in more detail, it's important to point out that professional refinishing is quite different to the DIY work which many car owners will have carried at home on a Sunday afternoon. Although much of the basic theory is the same, and many of the procedures are similar, the equipment and materials used for professional work are generally superior to those available for DIY use. Some modern finishes are extremely difficult to repair using DIY methods, and professional refinishing may be the only option for anything but the most minor damage.

Professional-standard refinishing is an art which cannot be learnt overnight, and whilst this book aims to provide a sound foundation, with plenty of tips and step-by-step procedures, there's no substitute for practical experience **(see illustration 1.1)**.

It's estimated that an average professional refinisher spends 70% of their time on preparation tasks,

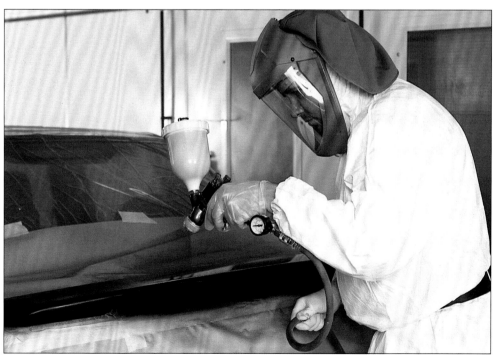

1.1 Spraying colour coat

whilst only 30% is actually spent applying paint. Bearing this in mind, it's important to understand that automotive paint refinishing involves far more than just spraying paint. The process includes surface preparation, primer applications, rubbing down and flatting, followed by colour coat spraying, and final polishing.

The future

The vehicle manufacturers' factory finishing processes are being constantly developed to improve efficiency, reduce cost, and to reduce VOC emissions into the atmosphere (see Chapter 4).

An example of this continual development is the recent use of powder-coat lacquer finishes, in which clear coat is applied to an electrostatically-charged panel in powder form, and then baked at temperatures of 180 to 200°C.

As the manufacturers' finishing processes develop, so the refinishing industry has to continually develop new processes, materials and techniques, to enable satisfactory repair work to be carried out.

Why are vehicles painted?

Vehicles are painted for two main reasons; firstly to protect the body panels against the elements, and secondly for the obvious cosmetic effect.

Protective qualities

Paint provides a water and pollution-resistant coating, which protects the material underneath it. Although a few vehicles may still contain mild-steel panels, almost all modern vehicles are made from galvanised steel panels (galvanising gives panels a protective coating which is resistant to corrosion – see Chapter 5). If mild-steel panels are not painted, they will rust very quickly, even without coming into contact with water, due to the moisture in the air. If galvanised panels are not painted, besides not being very attractive to look at, the panels will be vulnerable to stone chips which could damage the protective coating, allowing the bare metal underneath to rust.

Even though corrosion is not a problem on plastic and glass-fibre/GRP panels, paint is still normally applied to provide protection against pollution and scratches, and to give an attractive finish.

Cosmetic qualities

Modern paints allow a huge choice of colours and finishes, and colour and finish are important marketing tools for vehicle manufacturers. Colours are available in straightforward glosses and matts, and more exotic pearlescents and metallics. Paint technology and factory spraying techniques have become very advanced, and most vehicles now leave the factory with an excellent standard of paint finish and durability.

What is refinishing?

When a mass-produced vehicle is built at the factory, the body panels are coated with a protective layer to prevent corrosion, then painted on the production line. The painting process is normally automated, and most of the paint spraying is carried out by machines. The equipment and processes used are tailor-made for the particular model of vehicle on the production line, and the large number of vehicles passing through the factory enables the use of processes which would be far too expensive to carry out on a single vehicle.

Body shells and panels are painted at the factory before the engine, trim panels, upholstery, electronic components, etc, are fitted, and high temperatures can therefore be used to cure the paint.

When refinishing a vehicle in a body shop, it's not possible or desirable to use the methods used by the manufacturer when the vehicle is built. For example, when carrying out refinishing work, spraying must be carried out by hand, and because trim panels, electrical components, etc, will remain in position, high drying temperatures cannot be used.

Basically, refinishing replicates the processes used by the vehicle manufacturer during production, using alternative methods.

When carrying out a repair, the aim of the professional refinisher should be to achieve a repair which matches the original factory finish (which may not itself be perfect) so closely that the repair is impossible to detect.

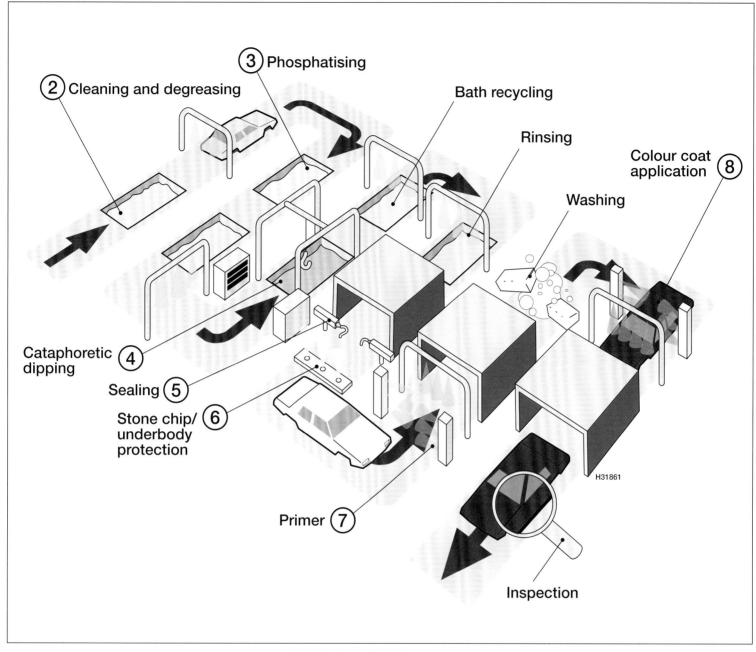

2 Cleaning and degreasing

3 Phosphatising

Bath recycling

Rinsing

Colour coat application **8**

Washing

Cataphoretic dipping **4**

Sealing **5**

Stone chip/ underbody protection **6**

Primer **7**

Inspection

H31861

1.2 Factory finishing process

1

Factory finishing

When a mass-produced vehicle is manufactured, the bodyshell and panels are treated and painted on the production line with no trim panels or ancillary equipment fitted. This obviously makes the initial coating and painting processes far easier than the equivalent refinishing operation.

The following paragraphs explain the steps used in a typical vehicle manufacturer's factory finishing process **(see illustration 1.2)**. Note that a typical process is shown, and the

individual steps and techniques are likely to differ from one manufacturer to another.

1 Galvanising

Galvanising involves coating a panel with a thin layer of zinc. The zinc layer will protect the metal underneath, even if there are tiny gaps or cracks in the coating, because oxygen will react more easily with zinc than with the bare exposed steel. Pre-galvanised panels are usually used in car construction.

The panels are coated with zinc either by immersion in hot molten zinc, or electrolytically. Panels which have been 'hot-dipped' can often be recognised by the zinc 'blooming' on the surface of the panel. Exterior panels which will later be painted are usually galvanised electrolytically, because this gives a smoother, more even coating.

Normally, panels would arrive on the production line pre-galvanised, and galvanising is not part of the production line process.

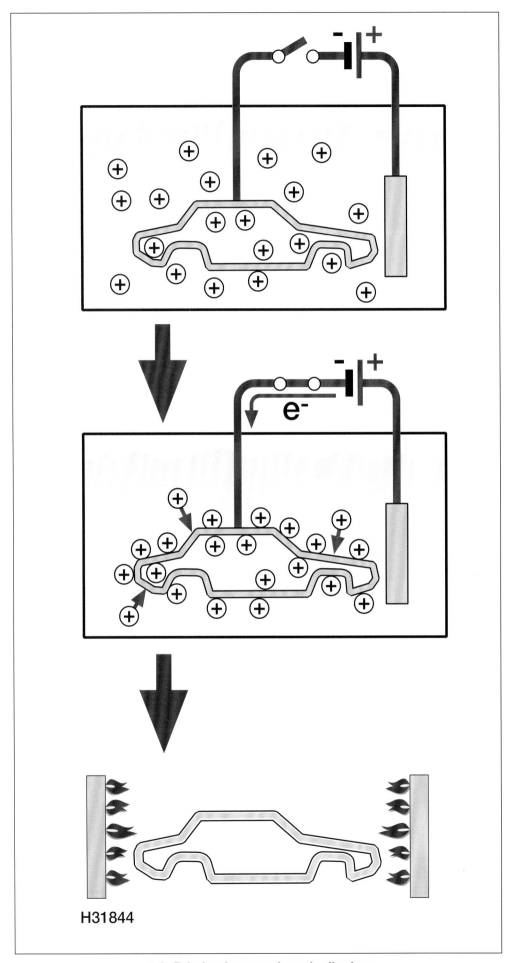

H31844

1.3 Priming by cataphoretic dipping

2 Cleaning and de-greasing

The first step in the production line finishing process is the cleaning and degreasing of the unpainted body panels. The body may be submerged in a bath of cleaning solution, and then sprayed with de-greasing solution. After rinsing and drying, any residues are removed from the panels.

3 Phosphatising

In the phosphatising process, the body is submerged in a bath containing a solution of various phosphate salts. Crystalline metal phosphates are deposited on the panels to give additional corrosion protection, and to provide a good base to enable paint to adhere.

4 Cataphoretic dipping

Cataphoresis (also known as *electrophoresis*) is an electrical process in which the body is submerged in a tank of paint/electrolyte solution **(see illustration 1.3)**. The body is connected to the negative terminal of a direct current electrical supply, and the positive terminal is connected to a series of plates (*anodes*) arranged around the tank. When the current is switched on, the positively-charged paint particles are attracted to the negatively-charged body, and an even layer of primer is distributed over the panels. Besides the fact that an even coating is produced, the advantage of this process it that all the metal surfaces of the body, internal, external, and hollow spaces, are coated with primer.

Once the body has been coated, it's removed from the bath and rinsed to remove any paint residues which have not adhered. The rinsed body is then dried in an oven to harden the primer.

It's worth noting that most manufacturers supply ready-primed replacement panels which have been primed using the cataphoretic dipping process.

The paint particles are electrostatically-charged and, instead of a conventional spray gun, special jets are used to spray the paint onto the electrostatically-charged body. This electrostatic process gives a very even finish, and uses far less paint than conventional spraying.

Once the primer has been sprayed, it's dried in an oven. When the paint has cured, and the panels have cooled, any necessary sanding can be carried out. The body is then cleaned to remove any sanding residue before the colour coat is applied.

8 Colour coat (base coat)

The colour coat is applied using a similar electrostatic process to the previous primer coat.

If a metallic or pearlescent colour coat is being applied, an automatic electronically-controlled spray gun may be used in conjunction with the electrostatic process to give a specific and even alignment of the metallic particles in the paint.

If no lacquer coat is to be applied, the colour coat is dried in an oven.

If a lacquer coat is to be applied, it will usually be applied before the colour coat has fully cured.

9 Clear (laquer) coat

Depending on the type of paint used for the colour coat (base coat), a coat of lacquer may now be sprayed to finish the painting process **(see illustration 1.4)**. The lacquer coat is sprayed before the colour coat cures fully, and combines with the colour coat to give a hard shiny film. The lacquer coat is applied using a similar electrostatic process to the primer and colour coats.

Once the lacquer coat has been applied, the finish is cured in an oven.

10 Wax cavity protection

To complete the finishing and corrosion protection process, any cavities and box sections in the metal bodywork are injected with corrosion-inhibiting wax or foam. This provides long-term corrosion protection, and also acts as noise insulation.

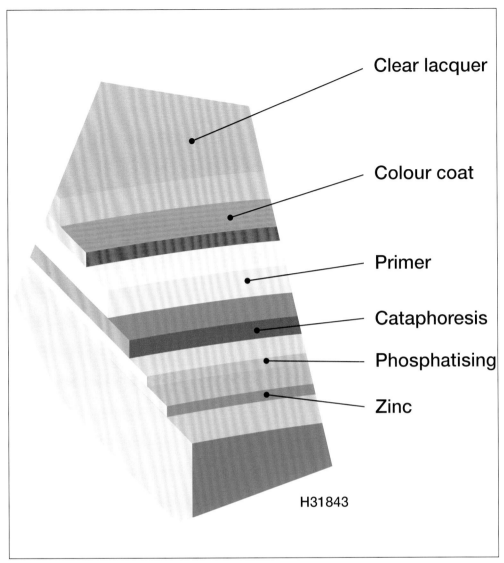

Clear lacquer

Colour coat

Primer

Cataphoresis

Phosphatising

Zinc

H31843

1.4 Finish layers applied during factory finishing

5 Sealing

At this stage in the process, joint sealer is applied to any overlaps and joints between metal panels, edges of panels, seam welds, etc. The sealer helps to stop corrosion by preventing water from entering the joints, and also reduces any noises which may be caused if panels were to move relative to each other during expansion or flexing.

6 Stone chip/underbody protection

After sealing, stone chip protection or underseal is normally sprayed onto areas such as the floor pan, wheel arches, sills, and sometimes the lower edges of wing panels, etc, which are susceptible to damage from flying stones. Stone chip paint is an elastic, thick, viscous paint, which is designed to absorb stone impacts without allowing the stones to penetrate through to the primer underneath.

7 Primer

A coat of primer is now sprayed to prime the body ready for the colour coat. The primer is used to smooth out any imperfections in the finish, and to provide a uniform surface for the colour coat.

The refinishing process

Health, safety and legislation

Many of the materials used during refinishing work can be harmful, both to humans and to the environment, and there's ever-tightening legislation which covers the storage, use and disposal of the various materials involved.

Although it's often tempting, *never* take any short-cuts where health and safety are concerned. The risks far outweigh any convenience or time-saving considerations.

Health and safety, and environmental legislation must be complied with, as inspectors have the power to impose heavy penalties, and can even prevent a refinishing centre from operating if they consider it necessary.

Health and safety considerations are dealt with in detail in Chapter 3, and details of the legislation covering professional refinishing work are covered in Chapter 4.

Preparation

The key to successful refinishing is preparation. There are a number of steps to be carried out before the final finish is applied, and each step is every bit as important as spraying the final top-coat **(see illustration 1.5)**. Any flaws or imperfections in the preparation will be exaggerated when the final finish is applied. Cleanliness is vital, and although time is precious in a body shop environment, short-cuts can lead to problems and extended job times, rather than saving time.

The process

The refinishing process begins by preparing the surface to be painted. The number and order of the steps to be carried out will depend on the extent of the damage (if any), the type of panel being refinished, and the type of paint to be used for the final finish.

If damage has occurred to the panel, reshaping or filling may be necessary and, if filler is used, it's important to use the correct type for the panel material being worked on (for example, not all fillers are suitable for use with galvanised steel).

Once the panel has been prepared for painting, the first stage of the painting process normally involves spraying an **etch primer**. The main purpose of etch primer is to provide resistance to corrosion; etch primer basically carries out the same function as the manufacturer's galvanising process.

At this point, any necessary stone-chip protection and sound-deadening protection is normally applied, although in some cases this can be left until the **high-build primer** has been applied (see following paragraph).

Once etch primer has been applied,

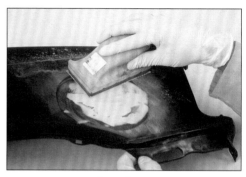

1.5 Sanding filler

a *high-build primer* is normally sprayed. The purpose of the high-build primer is to cover any imperfections in the surface of the panel, and to provide a base which can be worked to give a near-perfect surface, over which top-coat finish can be sprayed.

When the high-build primer surface has been worked to remove any imperfections, built-up areas and marks, and the surface finish is satisfactory, the **top-coat** colour can be sprayed. Various different types of top-coat colour finishes are available, both solvent-based, and water-based, and these are described in more detail in Chapter 7.

Once the top-coat colour has been applied, it may be necessary to spray a clear **lacquer** over the top of the colour.

When all the various layers of finish have been applied and cured, polishing can be carried out to produce the final high-gloss finish.

Materials

A wide range of materials is used during the refinishing process, and to anyone who is just starting a career in the industry, the range of products available can be somewhat daunting. Broadly speaking, the materials used can be divided into six main groups;

fillers, abrasives, paints and paint-related materials (primers, top-coats, lacquers, activators, thinners, etc), masking materials, cleaning materials, and flatting and polishing compounds.

When using any materials, it's important to avoid contamination. For example, if a full container of paint is accidentally contaminated, it may have to be discarded, which can prove to be an expensive mistake.

More detailed information on the materials used during the refinishing process are provided in Chapter 7.

Equipment

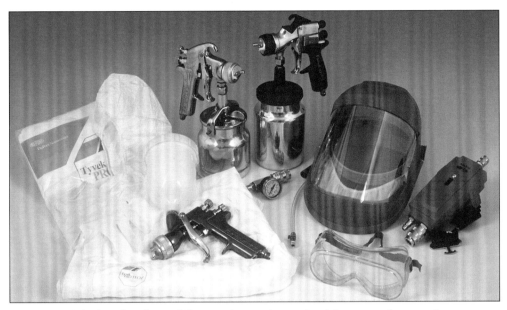

1.6 A selection of the equipment required for spraying work

Special equipment is essential when carrying out refinishing work, both to ensure a high-quality finish, and for health and safety reasons **(see illustration 1.6)**.

All professional refinishing centres use a spray booth and low-bake oven, which may be combined into one unit. Spray booths and low-bake ovens allow paint to be sprayed safely, provide a dust-free environment for spraying and drying the paint, and control emissions of harmful products into the atmosphere. When working in a spray booth, it's essential to wear appropriate safety equipment. As well as protective clothing, it's also necessary to use breathing apparatus to provide a supply of clean, filtered air.

Spray guns must be properly maintained, and suitable cleaning equipment must be available.

Appropriate personal safety equipment must be used at all times. Never take any risks where safety is concerned.

Other special equipment likely to be used during refinishing includes sanding/dust extraction equipment, polishers, paint agitators and mixers, infra-red drying lamps, etc.

Full details of the equipment used when carrying out refinishing work are given in Chapter 6.

1

Notes

Chapter 2
The theory of colour

Contents

Introduction

Before explaining the details of the refinishing process, it's useful to have a basic understanding of the theory of colour. Although there are many steps involved in the refinishing process, and the application of paint is the final stage in the process, all the painstaking preparation work will be in vain if the final colour sprayed in incorrect.

Hopefully, this Chapter will prove interesting, and will provide the reader with a sound background in the science of colour. This will be of help when colour matching, and will aid in understanding the reasons behind some of the procedures followed when spraying and checking the final finish.

What is colour?

The colour of an object depends on the human brain's interpretation of the signals produced by the eyes when an object is observed **(see illustration 2.1)**. The colour seen depends on several factors, such as the characteristics of the object, the ambient lighting, and the eye which is observing the object. When an object is observed, light illuminates the object, and the object reflects and absorbs the light in various ways, depending on the composition and the surface of the material from which the object is made. The eye receives the light reflected by the object, and sends information to the brain, which then interprets the information as form and colour.

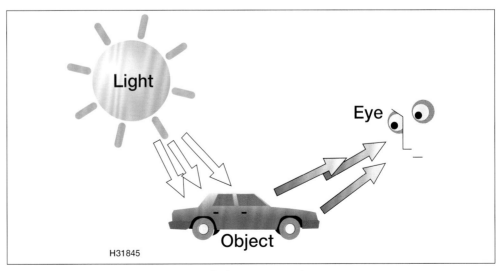

2.1 Colour perception

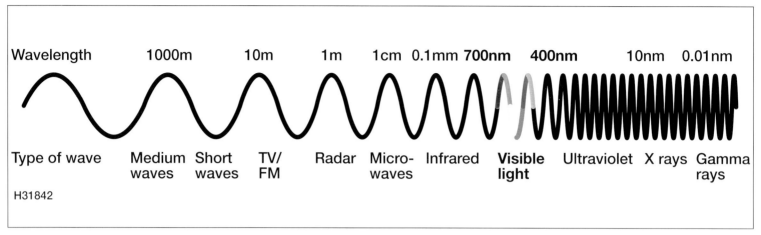

2.2 The electromagnetic spectrum

Visible light occupies a small section of the *electromagnetic spectrum*, falling between infra-red waves which have a wavelength higher than that of visible light, and ultra-violet, which has a wavelength shorter than visible light **(see illustration 2.2)**.

The human eye
A human eye contains millions of individual cells which react to light **(see illustration 2.3)**. The cells in the eye are

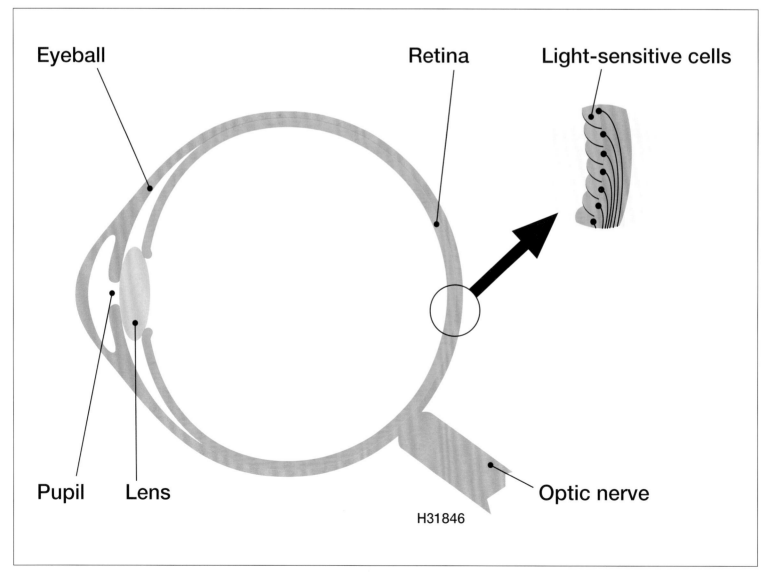

2.3 The human eye

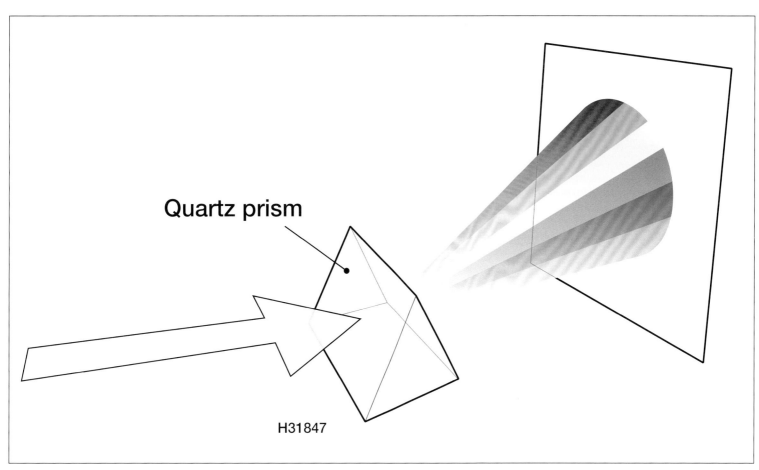

Quartz prism

H31847

2.4 The visible colour spectrum

stimulated by light, and send signals to the brain. The brain analyses all the information from the cells to produce the field of vision, giving form and colour to objects.

The eye contains four different types of cell, three of which are used to interpret colour:
• Cells sensitive to red light
• Cells sensitive to green light
• Cells sensitive to blue light
Colour perception is a result of the mixture of signals produced by these three types of cells. Cells of the fourth type, which are situated around the periphery of the visual field, are not colour-sensitive.

Colour blindness

A significant number of people suffer from a degree of colour blindness, which makes it difficult for them to tell certain colours apart. Colour blindness is usually due to problems with some of the previously-mentioned cells in the eye which are used to interpret colour. Most sufferers are only partially colour blind, and red and green are the colours which most

often give problems. Anyone who suffers from even partial colour blindness may find colour matching a very tricky operation. If you think that you may suffer from partial colour blindness, ask for professional advice (you may need to entrust colour matching to an experienced sprayer with normal colour vision).

Colour composition

All the colours which we can see are made up from various combinations of the seven colours of the rainbow (the *visible colour spectrum*); red, orange, yellow, green, blue, indigo and violet. White light is made up of all seven colours, and this can be seen when white light is shone through a transparent quartz prism and splits up into the colours of the r ainbow (this happens because different colours of light have different wavelengths, and are refracted at different angles by the prism) **(see illustration 2.4)**.

Different colours of light have different wavelengths, and the different wavelengths may be reflected or

absorbed by an object to different degrees. An object may absorb all of the light which it receives, or it may absorb some of the light and reflect the rest. The colour of an object depends on which wavelengths of light is absorbs, and which it reflects. For example;
• If white light hits an object which absorbs green and blue light, and reflects red light, the object will appear red.
• If white light hits an object which absorbs blue light, and reflects red and green light, the object will appear yellow.
• An object which reflects all the colours of the spectrum will appear white.

The effects of the ambient light

It's important to realise that the colour of an object depends on the light falling on it. Not all light is pure; for example daylight is bluish, and light from a tungsten light bulb is reddish. This means that objects may appear to

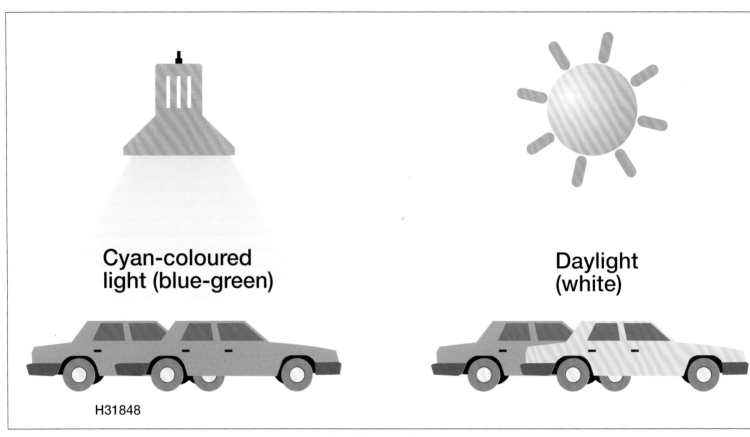

2.5 Metamerism

be a different colour when viewed in different lights **(see illustration 2.5)**.

It's possible to have two samples of a colour which look the same under a particular colour of light, but are in fact made up from different mixtures of pigments. When the two samples are viewed under a different light source, they may appear to be different colours. This effect is called *metamerism*.

An extreme example of this would be a resprayed area on a vehicle which is undetectable under body shop lighting conditions, but which stands out from the surrounding original paintwork in sunlight.

To prevent this problem, it's vital to make sure that the paint mixed up for a repair uses exactly the same pigments as the original paint on the vehicle.

Primary and secondary colours

Primary colours of light

As we've already seen, the human eye is sensitive to red, green and blue light, and any colour in the spectrum can be made by **adding** these three colours together in various combinations. A good example of this is a colour television, which uses red, green and blue 'colour guns' to produce the colours on the screen **(see illustration 2.6 opposite)**. So we can say that the *primary colours of light* are:

- Red
- Green
- Blue

A colour produced by adding two or three of the primary colours of light, is called an *additive colour mixture*, because primary colours are **added** to produce the colour mixture.

Primary pigment colours

Colours can also be made by **eliminating** various colours of light, such as when a particular substance absorbs certain colours (wavelengths) of light. For example if a material absorbs only red light, the colour seen will be a result of the signals produced by the cells in the eye which are sensitive to blue and green light (the cells sensitive to red light will not be stimulated because no red light is reflected by the object). For each of the primary colours of light, there is a *primary pigment colour*, which totally absorbs the relevant primary colour of light. The primary pigment colours are as follows:

- **Cyan** absorbs red light.
- **Magenta** absorbs green light.
- **Yellow** absorbs blue light.

As with the primary colours of light, any colour in the spectrum can be made by adding a combination of two or three of the primary pigment colours, cyan, magenta and yellow. For example, a mixture of cyan and yellow pigments will absorb red and blue light, and reflect green light. When the three primary pigment colours are mixed together, black or dark grey will result, because red, green and blue light is absorbed. (At this stage it's worth noting that, in practice, more than three colours are used in the paint mixing process, because in reality, not all colours can be easily mixed from the three primary colours.)

Cyan is actually a sky blue colour, and magenta is a form of red, so for the purposes of paint mixing, cyan pigment is often called blue, and magenta pigment is called red. Yellow pigment is pure yellow. This can be confusing, so once the theory of colour is understood, for the purposes of dealing with paints, we can forget about the *primary colours of light* (red, green and blue), and think in terms of pigment colours:

- **Blue** (Cyan) absorbs red light.
- **Red** (Magenta) absorbs green light.
- **Yellow** absorbs blue light.

Secondary pigment colours

Secondary pigment colours are produced when two of the primary pigment colours are added together in equal proportions.

- **Green** is produced when yellow and blue are added together.
- **Violet** is produced when blue and red are added together.
- **Orange** is produced when red and yellow are added together.

So the secondary pigment colours are green, violet and orange.

H31849

2.6 A colour television uses additive colour mixture to produce the colours on the screen

The pigment colour circle

The pigment colour circle consists of all the primary pigment colours, secondary pigment colours, and their mixtures. The colour circle basically represents all the colours which can be mixed from the primary colours: blue, red and yellow **(see illustration 2.7)**.

Complementary colours

Each of the primary pigment colours has a *complementary colour*; violet for yellow, orange for blue, and green for red. A complementary colour appears opposite its primary colour on the colour circle. If a primary colour and its complementary colour are mixed, eventually grey is produced.

Hues, tones, tints and shades

When dealing with paints, there are other more subtle groups of colours, known as *hues*, *tones*, *tints* and *shades*. These terms are used throughout the paint and refinishing industry, so it's a good idea to have a basic understanding of their meaning.

In the paint industry, a *hue* is usually considered to be a bright colour (eg, primary and secondary colours) such as red, blue or orange, etc.

If black is added to a hue, a *tone* of that hue is produced; for example if black is added to red (a hue), maroon (a tone of red) is produced **(see illustration 2.8)**.

If white is added to a hue, a *tint* of that hue is produced; for example if white is added to red (a hue), pink (a tint of red) is produced **(see illustration 2.9)**.

If a primary colour is mixed with its complementary colour, a *shade* of the primary colour is produced, and eventually grey is produced **(see illustration 2.10)**.

In summary :

Colour group	Composition
Hues	*Bright colours (red, blue, green, yellow, orange, violet, etc)*
Tones	*Hue + black*
Tints	*Hue + white*
Shade	*Primary colour + its complementary colour*

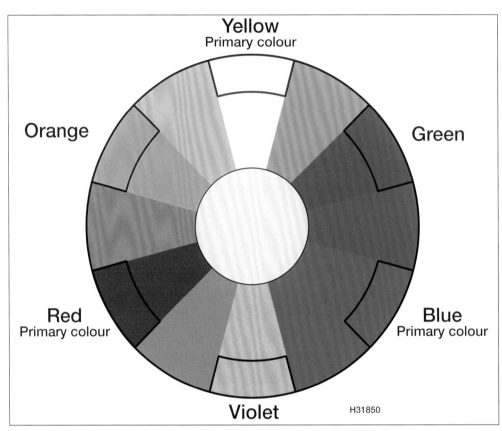

2.7 The pigment colour circle

2.8 Tones

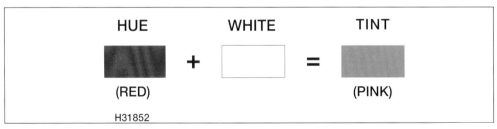

2.9 Tints

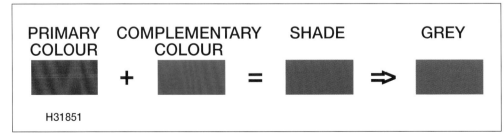

2.10 Shades

Colour variation

If refinishing work is to be carried out, the new paint to be used must be matched with the paint already on the vehicle. When trying to match paint, it's important to realise how a particular colour can vary.

There are basically three ways in which a specific colour can vary:

- Tone of colour.
- Purity of colour.
- Brightness of colour.

Variation in tone

Referring to the colour circle, a green colour can vary in the direction of blue or yellow. A green vehicle colour could therefore be a bluish or yellowish green.

Variation in purity

A green colour may be a pure green, or a 'dirtier' green. Again referring to the colour circle, the purer colours are found towards the outer circumference of the circle, and the 'dirtier' colours are found towards the centre of the circle. Colours become 'dirtier' due to mixing with other colours.

Variation in brightness

Although the tone and purity of a colour sample may be correct (ie, the sample fits in the correct location in the colour circle), a colour sample can vary in terms of brightness. For example a green colour can vary between dark green (darker paint) and light green (lighter paint). This variation may be due to the thickness of the paint layer, or ageing (fading).

Correcting colour variations

Colour correction can be carried out by adding base paint (a base paint is commonly known as a *tinter*). The base paint added is used to move the colour of the mixed paint in the appropriate direction on the colour circle to match the paint on the vehicle.

Clearly-defined colours (know as *chromatic* colours), such as reds and greens will often require tone and brightness corrections. Neutral colours (known as *achromatic* colours), such as whites, greys and beiges, often require purity corrections.

Tone correction

If the tone of a colour is incorrect, a base colour which counteracts the tone variation can be added to correct the tone. For example, if a sample of green paint is too yellow, a blue or bluish green base paint can be added to correct the tone.

Purity correction

To correct the purity of a colour, a base colour which is the exact opposite of the impurity in the colour circle is used (the complementary colour of the impurity). For example, if a sample of grey paint is too yellow, a violet or bluish base paint is added to correct the purity.

Brightness correction

When correcting the brightness of a colour, it may be necessary to darken the colour, or lighten the colour.

To **darken** the colour:

- For clearly defined colours, such as reds and greens (chromatic colours), a black base paint is added.
- For neutral colours, such as whites, greys and beiges (achromatic colours), the predominant chromatic base colour (red, green, etc) from the original paint formulation is added.

To **lighten** the colour:

- For non-metallic colours, a white base paint is added.
- For metallic colours, the metallic primary colour with the largest grain from the original paint formulation is added (white cannot be added, because it will cancel out the metallic effect).

2

Applying the theory

Hopefully, this Chapter has given a few clues to help to solve the mystery of colour.

Once the basic theory is understood, it will help in understanding why there are so many different colours of paint available. The theory can be applied when matching and mixing up colour coat, and when analysing faults with paintwork.

Notes

Chapter 3
Health and Safety

Contents

Introduction

Whenever any work is carried out on a vehicle, safety must always be the first consideration. In addition to the usual precautions which must be taken when working on any vehicle, refinishing operations present a range of additional hazards.

It's strongly suggested that the contents of this Chapter are read and thoroughly understood before attempting any of the work described in the following Chapters.

This Chapter is intended to provide a set of general guidelines for health and safety in the body shop. It does not attempt to provide a full set of health and safety recommendations.

General safety

Working on your car can be dangerous. This page shows just some of the potential risks and hazards, with the aim of creating a safety-conscious attitude.

General hazards

Scalding
• Don't remove the radiator or expansion tank cap while the engine is hot.
• Engine oil, automatic transmission fluid or power steering fluid may also be dangerously hot if the engine has recently been running.

Burning
• Beware of burns from the exhaust system and from any part of the engine. Brake discs and drums can also be extremely hot immediately after use.

Crushing
• When working under or near a raised vehicle, always supplement the jack with axle stands, or use drive-on ramps.
Never venture under a car which is only supported by a jack.
• Take care if loosening or tightening high-torque nuts when the vehicle is on stands. Initial loosening and final tightening should be done with the wheels on the ground.

Fire
• Fuel is highly flammable; fuel vapour is explosive.

• Don't let fuel spill onto a hot engine.
• Do not smoke or allow naked lights (including pilot lights) anywhere near a vehicle being worked on. Also beware of creating sparks (electrically or by use of tools).
• Fuel vapour is heavier than air, so don't work on the fuel system with the vehicle over an inspection pit.
• Another cause of fire is an electrical overload or short-circuit. Take care when repairing or modifying the vehicle wiring.
• Keep a fire extinguisher handy, of a type suitable for use on fuel and electrical fires.

Electric shock
• Ignition HT voltage can be dangerous, especially to people with heart problems or a pacemaker. Don't work

on or near the ignition system with the engine running or the ignition switched on.

• Mains voltage is also dangerous. Make sure that any mains-operated equipment is correctly earthed. Mains power points should be protected by a residual current device (RCD) circuit breaker.

Fume or gas intoxication

• Exhaust fumes are poisonous; they often contain carbon monoxide, which is rapidly fatal if inhaled. Never run the engine in a confined space such as a garage with the doors shut.

• Fuel vapour is also poisonous, as are the vapours from some cleaning solvents and paint thinners.

Poisonous or irritant substances

• Avoid skin contact with battery acid and with any fuel, fluid or lubricant, especially antifreeze, brake hydraulic fluid and Diesel fuel. Don't syphon them by mouth. If such a substance is swallowed or gets into the eyes, seek medical advice.

• Prolonged contact with used engine oil can cause skin cancer. Wear gloves or use a barrier cream if necessary. Change out of oil-soaked clothes and do not keep oily rags in your pocket.

• Air conditioning refrigerant forms a poisonous gas if exposed to a naked flame (including a cigarette). It can also cause skin burns on contact.

Asbestos

• Asbestos dust can cause cancer if inhaled or swallowed. Asbestos may be found in gaskets and in brake and clutch linings. When dealing with such components it is safest to assume that they contain asbestos.

Special hazards

Hydrofluoric acid

• This extremely corrosive acid is formed when certain types of synthetic rubber, found in some O-rings, oil seals, fuel hoses etc, are exposed to temperatures above 400°C. The rubber changes into a charred or sticky substance containing the acid. Once formed, the acid remains dangerous for years. If it gets onto the skin, it may be necessary to amputate the limb concerned.

• When dealing with a vehicle which has suffered a fire, or with components salvaged from such a vehicle, wear protective gloves and discard them after use.

The battery

• Batteries contain sulphuric acid, which attacks clothing, eyes and skin. Take care when topping-up or carrying the battery.

• The hydrogen gas given off by the battery is highly explosive. Never cause a spark or allow a naked light nearby. Be careful when connecting and disconnecting battery chargers or jump leads.

Air bags

• Air bags can cause injury if they go off accidentally. Take care when removing the steering wheel and/or facia. Special storage instructions may apply.

Diesel injection equipment

• Diesel injection pumps supply fuel at very high pressure. Take care when working on the fuel injectors and fuel pipes.

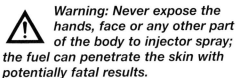

Warning: Never expose the hands, face or any other part of the body to injector spray; the fuel can penetrate the skin with potentially fatal results.

Remember...

DO

• Do use eye protection when using power tools, and when working under the vehicle.

• Do wear gloves or use barrier cream to protect your hands when necessary.

• Do get someone to check periodically that all is well when working alone on the vehicle.

• Do keep loose clothing and long hair well out of the way of moving mechanical parts.

• Do remove rings, wristwatch etc, before working on the vehicle – especially the electrical system.

• Do ensure that any lifting or jacking equipment has a safe working load rating adequate for the job.

DON'T

• Don't attempt to lift a heavy component which may be beyond your capability – get assistance.

• Don't rush to finish a job, or take unverified short cuts.

• Don't use ill-fitting tools which may slip and cause injury.

• Don't leave tools or parts lying around where someone can trip over them. Mop up oil and fuel spills at once.

• Don't allow children or pets to play in or near a vehicle being worked on.

Refinishing safety precautions

The hazards

When working with refinishing materials and equipment, there are certain specific hazards, which require special precautions to be taken.

• **Dust**. A large amount of dust is created during sanding operations. Dust can cause respiratory problems, and some of the chemicals present in filler and paint can be poisonous. It's important to take suitable precautions. Always use dust extraction equipment, where possible, and always wear a dust mask when carrying out sanding work.

• **Solvents**. Solvents are very volatile, and present a serious health and fire hazard. They are also a hazard to the environment. Solvents should only be used in well-ventilated areas, and when spraying materials containing solvents, an air-fed breathing mask should be worn at all times. Ensure that all regulations concerning the storage, use and disposal of solvents have been read and understood. Refer to Chapter 4 for details of legislation which applies to the use of solvents.

Safety clothing and equipment

When carrying out refinishing work, it's essential to use appropriate safety clothing and equipment at all times **(see illustration 3.1)**.

• **Always wear non-absorbent gloves** when carrying out any refinishing work, or when handling products containing solvents.

• **Always wear overalls or a protective coat, and don't work with bare arms**. Don't be tempted to work with rolled-up sleeves, even on a hot day.

• **Wear safety shoes or boots** when handling heavy equipment.

• **Wear a chemical protective suit with a hood and an air-fed breathing mask** when working in a spray booth.

• **Wear safety goggles** when carrying out machine sanding, compounding or polishing work.

• **Wear a dust mask** when carrying out sanding work.

3.1 A range of safety clothing and equipment is required during refinishing work

Do's and don'ts

DO

• Do wear non-absorbent gloves when carrying out any refinishing work.

• Do keep loose clothing and long hair clear of power tools.

• Do ensure adequate ventilation at all times when working with solvents.

• Do ensure that anyone working in the vicinity is aware of the hazards present. (No smoking, no naked flames, no welding, no working in inspection pits, etc).

• Do use dust extraction equipment when carrying out sanding operations.

• Do store all materials in accordance with the relevant material safety data sheet.

• Do refit lids to all material containers when not in use. This will help to avoid contamination, and will prevent unnecessary vapour release.

• Do seal any open fuel line connections before drying a vehicle in a low-bake oven.

• Do slacken the fuel filler cap before drying a vehicle in a low-bake oven.

• Do always read the safety recommendations on product packaging.

DON'T

• Don't smoke in a body shop.

• Don't use a space heater when working in a body shop.

• Don't carry out welding work in a refinishing area.

• Don't be tempted to work with the visor up when wearing an air-fed breathing mask.

• Don't use non-approved electrical equipment (eg, extra lights) in a spray booth (spray booth electrical equipment meets stringent insulation regulations to prevent the possibility of sparks).

Materials Safety Data Sheets

All chemical-based products used in the refinishing industry have a relevant Materials Safety Data Sheet (MSDS), which will give a set of recommendations for handling and storage, fire fighting methods, necessary personal protective equipment, first aid, etc **(see illustration 3.2)**.

These data sheets must be held in the body shop and must be able to be accessed quickly for reference in the event of an accident.

10068 - 2K Extra Clear Lacquer

SAFETY DATA SHEET
2K Extra Clear Lacquer

1. IDENTIFICATION OF THE SUBSTANCE/PREPARATION AND THE COMPANY:

PRODUCT NAME: 2K Extra Clear Lacquer

PART No.:   003230

APPLICATIONS: Paint Lacquer.

SUPPLIER: Tetrosyl (Sales) Ltd.
                          Bevis Green Works
                          Bury
                          Lancs. BL9 6RE
TELEPHONE: 0161 764-5981
FAX: 0161 763-5877

2. COMPOSITION/INFORMATION ON INGREDIENTS:

INGREDIENT NAME:	CAS No.:	CONTENT	HEALTH:	RISK:
BUTYL ACETATE	123-86-4	10-30 %		
TOLUENE	108-88-3	10-30 %	Xn	20
PETROLEUM DISTILLATE	64742-95-6	10-30 %		

3. HAZARDS IDENTIFICATION:

Highly flammable. Harmful by inhalation, in contact with skin and if swallowed. Irritating to skin. May cause sensitisation by inhalation.

4. FIRST AID MEASURES:

GENERAL: No recommendation given, but first aid may still be required in case of accidental exposure, inhalation or ingestion of this chemical. If in doubt, GET MEDICAL ATTENTION PROMPTLY!

INHALATION: Remove victim immediately from source of exposure. General first aid, rest, warmth and fresh air. If severe: Apply Artificial respiration.

INGESTION: Drink a few glasses of water or milk. DO NOT INDUCE VOMITING! Get medical attention.

SKIN: Wash the skin immediately with soap and water.

EYES: Important! Immediately rinse with water for 15-30 minutes. Get medical attention if any discomfort continues.

5. FIRE FIGHTING MEASURES:

EXTINGUISHING MEDIA:
      Use: Foam. Powder. Carbon dioxide (CO2). Do not use Water Jets.

SPECIAL FIRE FIGHTING PROCEDURES:
      Fire can be extinguished using: Foam. Powder Carbon dioxide (CO2). Firefighters wear self-contained breathing apparatus.

1 / 4

3.2 Typical Materials Safety Data Sheet

Chapter 4
Legislation

Contents

Introduction

When working in a body shop environment, various legislation must be taken into account when using equipment and handling materials. Aside from health and safety issues (which are broadly covered in Chapter 3), the main area of legislation which is of concern is the area covering damage to the environment.

As part of the worldwide effort to reduce damage to the environment, many countries have introduced legislation to reduce the emissions of Volatile Organic Compounds (VOCs, described later in this Chapter) into the

atmosphere. In recent years, legislation has been introduced in the UK to control the emission of VOCs from automotive body shops.

UK legislation is usually developed from European Commission (EC) Directives, often with detailed changes and/or additions. Thus, although UK legislation is broadly in keeping with that in the rest of Europe, on the whole it is more stringent than that found in may other European countries.

Legislation is constantly changing, and recently, with the arrival of devolution in the UK, separate

regulations exist for England, Scotland, Wales and Northern Ireland. The best way of finding out exactly what legislation applies to a particular body shop is to contact the appropriate local authority. Local authority inspectors are responsible for policing the regulations in their area.

This Chapter cannot hope to provide a detailed description of all the relevant rules and regulations which must be observed, but it aims to cover some of the more important points.

Volatile Organic Compounds (VOCs)

What are VOCs?

Volatile Organic Compounds (VOCs) are chemical substances which rise into the atmosphere and react with nitrogen oxides to produce ozone. Although ozone is desirable in the upper atmosphere to protect the earth's surface from harmful ultra-violet radiation, excess ozone in the lower atmosphere is undesirable, and is a major cause of air pollution.

The most significant source of VOCs is chemical solvents. Solvent is a general term, and when applied to paint products refers to the material used to keep the paint in a liquid state. Various solvents may be used during other stages of the refinishing process, for example thinners, panel wipe and spray gun cleaner. A container of solvent-based paint could contain 90% solvent, whilst thinners are often 100% solvent.

Tightening legislation is forcing the paint manufacturers to produce paints containing lower quantities of solvents.

The current trend in paint technology is towards the use of water-based paints, instead of solvent-based paints (note that water-based paints still contain solvent). In the near future, it's possible that all automotive paints will be water-based.

VOC compliant coatings

VOC compliant coatings are refinishing products which meet the current EPA regulations (explained later in this Chapter) regarding the level of solvents which they contain.

The current VOC limits as at 1st April 2000 are as follows (all quantities are measured in grams of solvent per litre of product):

Product	VOC limit
Gun wash	850
Panel wipe	200
Primer surfacer	250
Wet-on-wet primer	540
Top-coats	420
Clear-coat	420
Special products	840

These limits are likely to change, and are currently only applicable to the UK. It is possible that some limits may actually be raised in the future due to the difficulty in developing coatings which work satisfactorily within the current low limits.

High Volume Low Pressure (HVLP) spraying

Almost all modern spray guns work on the High Volume Low Pressure (HVLP) principle, using air pressures of around 10 psi, whereas older spraying equipment is designed to work at air pressures of around 50 to 60 psi. HVLP spraying enables more paint to adhere to panels, with far less overspray than that produced by high-pressure spraying techniques. Since more paint sticks to the panels, less is wasted through clouds of spray ricocheting off the panel into the atmosphere, and hence VOC emissions are reduced.

Environmental Protection Act (EPA)

In the UK the Environmental Protection Act (EPA) provides legislation concerning the release of VOCs into the atmosphere from body shops.

At the time of writing, the legislation in force in the UK states that any body shop which has an annual VOC consumption of more than one tonne must register with the local authority, although this is likely to change in the future. Body shops with an annual VOC consumption of less than one tonne are exempt from EPA regulations.

A brief summary of the major points of UK EPA regulations as they stand at the 1st April 2000 is as follows:

• All coatings used must be VOC compliant.
• HVLP spray guns must be used for all coatings.
• Gun cleaning and similar operations

must be carried out in an automatic, fully-enclosed equipment cleaning machine, or any equipment that can achieve comparable or lower emissions.
• A record must be kept of all paint, hardener, organic solvent and cleaning materials used. Copies of the records showing the total quantities of organic solvent usage should be submitted to the local authority every 6 months.
• All paint spraying should be carried out in a totally enclosed booth.
• Spray booths must operate under negative pressure, and must shut-down automatically if a positive pressure develops.
• The exhaust chimney height of the spray booth must be three metres above the roof ridge height of any

building within 15 metres of the base of the chimney.
• Regular particulate emission testing must be carried out to ensure that a spray booth meets EPA VOC emission regulations.
• Spray booths must comply fully with EPA legislation.
• All power tools and welding equipment must be fitted with dust/fume extraction apparatus.

The EPA also contains legislation which applies to materials handling and storage, and the disposal of waste from the refinishing processes.

If it's found that a body shop is breaking EPA regulations, local authority inspectors have the power to prevent the body shop from operating, and in severe cases, heavy fines can be imposed on the operators.

The future

Future legislation is likely to become more stringent. In the UK, a new act called the Pollution Prevention and Control Act is likely to progressively supercede the EPA between the time of writing and 2007.

Future EC regulation which may be adopted in the UK states that all body shops using more than 500kg of solvents per year must register with their local authority. Eventually it's likely that instead of basing legislation on the quantity of solvents used, legislation will be product-based, which means that all body shops, regardless of size, must comply. The ultimate aim of future legislation is to reduce the level of solvents used to zero.

Notes

Chapter 5
Substrates

Contents

Introduction

In the world of automotive refinishing, 'substrate' is basically a term for the base material to which a paint finish is applied. The base material is likely to be metal, plastic or fibreglass.

The type of substrate to be repaired may affect the type of materials used during the repair process. For example, some body fillers are not suitable for use on galvanised metal, and some types of primer paints will not adhere easily to certain plastics. On the whole, the repair procedures themselves will be unaffected by the type of substrate.

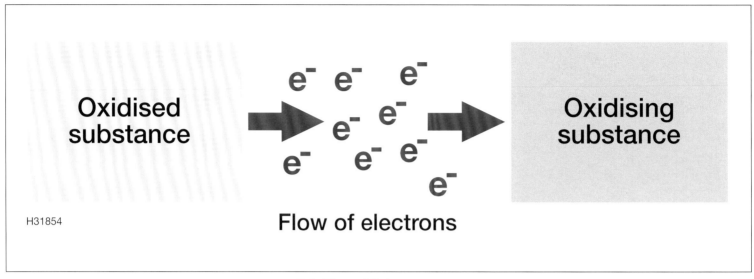

5.1 The oxidising process

Corrosion

General

Corrosion only causes a problem with metal substrates; glass-fibre/GRP and plastic substrates do not require corrosion protection, and are painted purely for cosmetic reasons, and to prevent contamination. (Note that some fibreglass panels are impregnated with a coloured resin during manufacture, and are not spray-painted in the conventional manner.)

Steel oxidation

Most vehicle bodies are constructed from steel, which is susceptible to oxidation (corrosion).

Oxidation is a chemical process, in which electrons are exchanged between two different substances. The atoms of the substance which is being oxidised release electrons, and the atoms of the oxidising substance absorb those electrons **(see illustration 5.1)**. The tendency to release or absorb electrons varies between substances.

Certain metals, such as iron, tend to release electrons easily, and therefore oxidise (corrode) easily. Some other metals, such as copper, release electrons less easily, and will only oxidise when brought into contact with a strong oxidising substance. A few metals, such as gold, will only oxidise under very extreme conditions (they also tend to be very expensive!).

A substance which oxidises easily (such as iron) is said to have a strong oxidation tendency, and a substance which does not easily oxidise (such as gold) is said to have a low oxidation tendency. If two substances with different oxidation tendencies are brought into contact, electrons will tend to flow from the substance with the higher oxidation tendency to the substance with the lower oxidation tendency **(see illustration 5.2)**. The higher a substance's oxidation tendency, the more prone the substance is to corrosion.

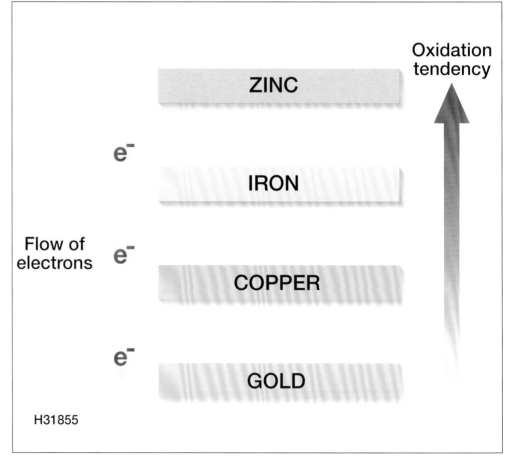

5.2 Oxidation tendencies

Mild steel

Mild steel is essentially bare, untreated metal; ie, it has no corrosion protection. Mild steel will corrode in air, because the oxygen in the air oxidises the metal. Rust is basically red iron oxide.

In recent years, mild steel has been superseded by galvanised steel for body panels on most modern vehicles. There are however still a large number of vehicles in use which are fitted with mild steel panels.

Mild steel can be recognised from the fact that it will oxidise (rust) in contact with the moisture in air in a matter of hours.

Galvanised steel

Galvanised steel is steel which has been chemically treated to coat the surfaces with a protective layer which guards against corrosion (see Chapter 1). Almost all modern vehicles use galvanised steel panels. The galvanising process ensures that all the surfaces of the panel are coated, regardless of how complicated the panel shape.

Galvanising involves coating a panel with a thin layer of zinc. The zinc layer will protect the metal underneath even if there are tiny gaps or cracks in the coating, because zinc will oxidise more easily than the bare exposed metal. Although zinc oxidises more readily than steel, it does so more slowly, and the steel will only begin to oxidise (corrode) once all the zinc has completely oxidised away **(see illustration 5.3)**.

There are various different methods of galvanising, but the most common methods are the 'hot dip' process, and the electrolytic process. In the hot dip process, the panels are first dipped in acid to remove dirt and grease, and then dipped in molten zinc. In the electrolytic process, an electric current is passed between two electrodes immersed in a zinc salt solution; the panel forms the negative electrode, and as the current flows, zinc is deposited to coat the surfaces of the panel.

5

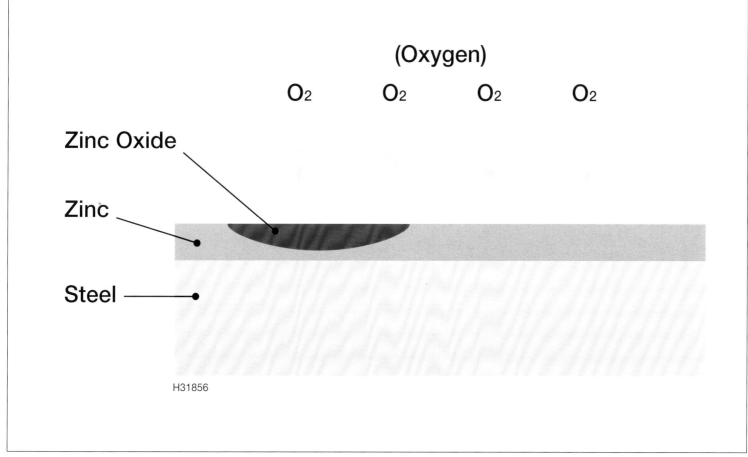

(Oxygen)

O_2 O_2 O_2 O_2

Zinc Oxide

Zinc

Steel

H31856

5.3 Galvanised steel will only begin to oxidise once all the zinc has oxidised away

Aluminium

Aluminium panels are used on some vehicle, notably some Land Rovers and Audi models. Aluminium is less susceptible to oxidation than steel, but still requires a similar degree of corrosion protection.

When fitting new aluminium panels, care must be taken to insulate them from surrounding steel panels and/or fittings such as bolts and rivets. This is because, as we've already seen, if two substances with different oxidation tendencies are brought into contact, electrons will tend to flow from the substance with the higher oxidation tendency to the substance with the lower oxidation tendency, causing corrosion.

In most cases, when refinishing aluminium panels, exactly the same processes and materials are used as when refinishing galvanised steel panels.

Glass-fibre/GRP

Glass-fibre and GRP (glass-reinforced plastic) is used for the manufacture of body panels on some low-volume production cars, and numerous kit-cars. These panels are not susceptible to oxidation.

Most manufacturers use a factory finishing process similar to a typical refinishing process, with layers of primer, colour coat and, where applicable, a lacquer coat. Such panels can be refinished in the conventional way. Check that any body filler used is compatible with fibreglass panels.

A 'gel-coat' finish is normally used during the manufacture of glass-fibre and GRP panels. The gel-coat is actually a layer of resin, with colour pigment added, which is poured into the mould before the layers of material are built up to form the panel. No primer is used with a gel-coat finish, and the finish is actually part of the panel structure. Refinishing can still be carried out in the conventional manner.

When spraying top-coat finish over glass-fibre and GRP panels, it may be necessary to add a flexible additive to allow for flexing of the panel. It's also important to take care not to use too high a baking temperature when drying paint on glass-fibre and GRP panels; excessive temperatures could distort or even melt panels.

Plastics

Plastic panels are used extensively on many modern mass-produced vehicles, particularly for components such as bumpers, grille panels, etc. Some vehicles (notably some Citroëns) may also be fitted with plastic bonnets, tailgate panels, etc, as a weight-saving measure.

Conventional refinishing procedures can be used on plastic panels, but note that with certain plastics, it may be necessary to use an adhesion promoter in order to enable the paint to adhere to the plastic. Some paint products may require the addition of a flexible additive to prevent the finish from cracking as the plastic panel flexes (recommendations will be given on the paint manufacturer's technical data/application sheet).

Chapter 6
Equipment

Contents

Introduction

A wide range of specialist equipment is used for refinishing work, and such equipment is essential to achieve professional results safely, and in line with current legislation (see Chapter 4).

Always ensure that any equipment used is treated with respect, and is properly maintained in accordance with the manufacturer's recommendations; this applies particularly to spray guns and spray booths/low-bake ovens.

Before using a new piece of equipment for the first time, ensure that you are familiar with the equipment controls and operating procedures.

Personal safety equipment

Overalls

Always wear suitable lint-free overalls when carrying out refinishing work. This will not only protect skin and clothes, but will also prevent any loose particles from clothing causing contamination problems.

When carrying out spraying work, suitable non-absorbent overalls with a hood must be worn (ensure that the overalls are suitable for use when spraying solvents). To avoid contamination, don't carry out flatting/sanding work, or any other kind of work which involves dust, whilst wearing the overalls which will be worn in the spray booth.

Gloves

Latex gloves should be worn when handling paint materials and when carrying out spraying work. This will protect the skin, and will also prevent any moisture and greases present in the skin from contaminating materials or paintwork.

Footwear

Whenever working in a workshop environment, safety shoes should be worn to protect against chemicals and to protect the feet against crushing. When working in a spray booth, it's advisable to wear suitable plastic or rubber overshoes to prevent contamination, and damage to shoes from overspray.

Goggles

Always wear safety goggles when carrying out flatting and sanding work, and when spraying (unless a full-face air-fed mask is used).

Dust masks and breathing apparatus

When carrying out flatting and sanding work, or any other work which involves the release of dust into the atmosphere, a suitable dust mask should be worn. Make sure that the mask is suitable for the task for which it is being used – instructions are usually supplied with the packaging **(see illustration 6.1)**.

When working in a spray booth, an air-fed mask should be worn. An air-fed mask isolates the sprayer from the air in the spray booth, and provides a filtered supply of fresh breathing air (from the same source as the air supply to the spray gun). The visor should be pulled down over the face at all times when spraying. Note that air-fed masks have an air filter in the air line to the mask which must be changed at the manufacturer's recommended intervals.

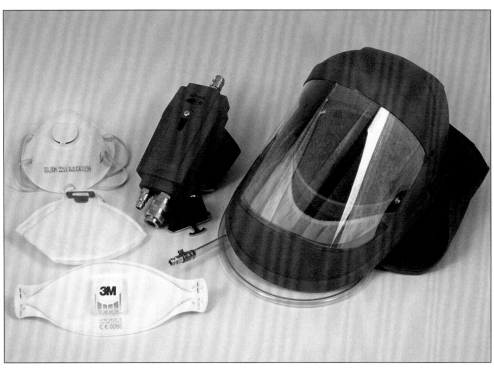

6.1 A selection of dust masks and (air-fed) breathing apparatus

Spray guns

Refer to Chapter 8 for details of spray guns.

Compressors

General

Various different types of compressor are available, but the most common types likely to be found in a modern body shop are the piston compressor, the rotary vane compressor and the screw compressor.

Compressors may be driven by an electric motor, a petrol engine, or a diesel engine, although most industrial compressors are electrically-driven.

Compressor controls vary in complexity, from simple manual controls to fully automatic control systems which vary the motor speed to suit air demand.

Compressors are normally used in conjunction with an air receiver (reservoir) which will provide a reserve of air in excess of the continuous output of the compressor (to cope with any sudden increase in demand), and will smooth out any pulses in the air supply. Additionally, an air drying (or air conditioning) system may be fitted to remove moisture from the air supply.

Piston compressor

Piston compressors have one or more piston(s). Each cylinder of a piston compressor goes through an air intake stroke, followed by a combined compression/exhaust stroke. Low pressure air is drawn into the cylinder through an intake valve as the piston moves down the cylinder during the intake stroke. As the piston moves back up the cylinder on the compression stroke, the air is compressed. When a pre-set pressure is reached, the exhaust valve opens to allow the air to move out of the compressor cylinder towards the air reservoir **(see illustration 6.2)**.

6

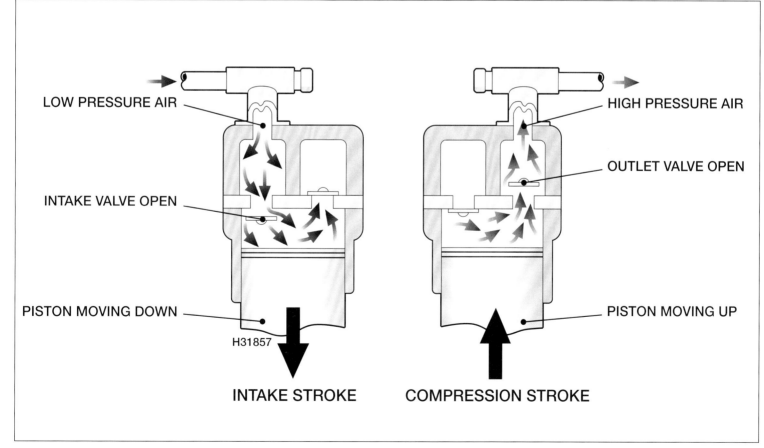

LOW PRESSURE AIR

INTAKE VALVE OPEN

PISTON MOVING DOWN

H31857

INTAKE STROKE

HIGH PRESSURE AIR

OUTLET VALVE OPEN

PISTON MOVING UP

COMPRESSION STROKE

6.2 Piston compressor operation

Rotary vane compressor

Rotary vane-type compressors consist of a rotor with several vanes, which run in an offset cylindrical housing. As the compressor shaft rotates, the vanes and housing form chambers. The air is drawn through the intake port into the chambers, which reduce in size as the rotor turns. The outlet port is located at the point where the chambers are at their smallest, where the vapour is completely compressed **(see illustration 6.3)**. The vanes slide in and out of the rotor in precision-machined slots, on a film of oil.

Vane compressors have no sealing rings. The vanes are sealed against the housing by centrifugal force and lubricating oil. The lubricating oil sump is located on the outlet side of the compressor, so the high pressure tends to force the oil around the edges of the vanes into the low pressure side. This action ensures continuous lubrication, and helps to cool the compressed air. After the air has been compressed, the oil is removed by an oil separation system to provide a supply of clean air.

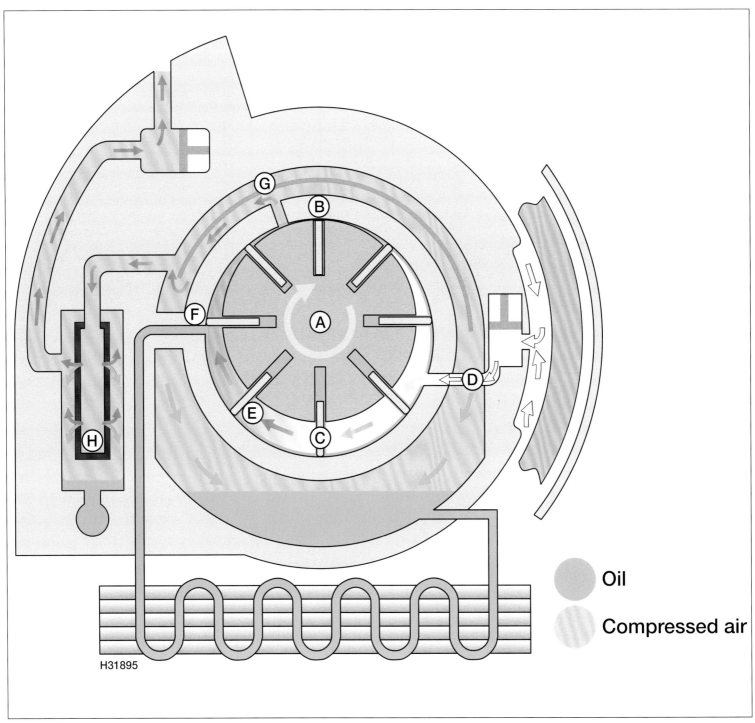

H31895

6.3 Rotary vane compressor operation

A Rotor
B Rotor housing
C Vane

D Air inlet
E Compression
    chamber

F Oil inlet
G Air/oil outlet
H Oil separator

6.4 Screw compressor helical rotors

A Female (fluted) rotor   B Male (lobed) rotor

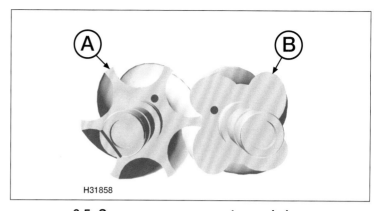

6.5 Screw compressor rotor end view

A Female (fluted) rotor   B Male (lobed) rotor

Screw compressor

Screw compressors are quieter in operation, and suffer from less vibration than other compressor types. Screw compressors are built to very fine tolerances, and have a number of integrated sub-systems which work together to supply cool, dry compressed air.

A screw compressor consists of two helically-cut intermeshing rotors mounted in a close fitting housing. The male rotor normally has four lobes, and the female rotor normally has six flutes **(see illustrations 6.4 and 6.5)**. The male rotor is gear driven by an electric motor, and the female rotor is driven by the male rotor, via a cushion of air/oil. Oil is injected into the air as it enters the rotor housing. The oil provides lubrication, provides a seal between the rotors and the housing, and acts as a coolant (a large amount of heat is produced during the compression process).

Air is compressed between the lobes of the male rotor, and the flutes on the female rotor and the rotor housing (stator). The tips of the male rotor lobes incorporate sealing strips to provide as close a seal as possible during operation. The female rotor and the housing can be considered to be a cylinder, with the male rotor acting as a piston to compress the air/oil mixture.

As the rotors rotate, a delivery port is uncovered, and the compressed air/oil mixture leaves the rotor housing, and passes to an oil separator system, which separates the oil from the air. After leaving the oil separator, the air passes through a cooler, and finally through a moisture separator, before entering the air supply system **(see illustration 6.6)**.

6

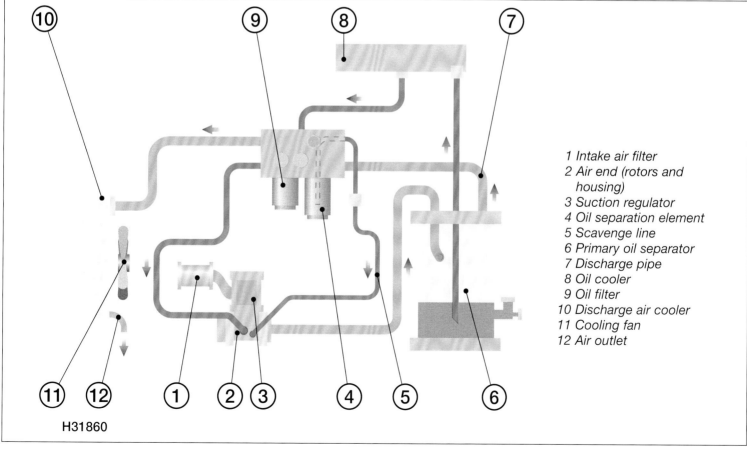

1 Intake air filter
2 Air end (rotors and housing)
3 Suction regulator
4 Oil separation element
5 Scavenge line
6 Primary oil separator
7 Discharge pipe
8 Oil cooler
9 Oil filter
10 Discharge air cooler
11 Cooling fan
12 Air outlet

H31860

6.6 Schematic layout of a typical screw compressor

Maintenance

All compressors require routine maintenance, and they should be maintained in accordance with the manufacturer's recommendations. Regular maintenance is essential to ensure that the air is of suitable quality for spraying (and breathing).

Essential regular maintenance usually includes the following:

- Water trap emptying
- Oil level checking
- Oil changing
- Intake air filter cleaning or renewal
- Oil separator filter cleaning or renewal
- Drivebelt tensioning (when applicable)

Note that engine oil is not generally suitable for compressor lubrication. Use only the oil specified by the manufacturer.

Failure to carry out regular compressor maintenance can result in problems when spraying, such as moisture and/or particle contamination in the air supply, and inconsistent spraying pressure.

Selecting a compressor

Every air tool, spray guns included, requires a certain volume of air per minute at a certain pressure. The volume, or flow, is expressed in cubic feet per minute (cfm) or litres per minute (l/min). The pressure is expressed in pounds per square inch (psi) or bars. Compressor output is expressed in the same units.

Compressor capacity should be comfortably in excess of the total requirements of all the tools liable to be in use at any one time, calculated by adding together their airflow requirements. Consider also whether more tools may be added at a later date. Note that there may be a considerable difference between the compressor's nominal delivery capacity (air displacement) and the actual delivery capacity (free air delivered). The volume of the air receiver (reservoir) must also be considered. There are complex choices to be made here; if in doubt, advice should be sought from the compressor manufacturer.

There are two types of compressor drive: direct and via a belt. Direct drive compressors are less expensive and potentially more efficient than belt-driven, but generally have a shorter working life. For professional and industrial applications, where the compressor is liable to be in use for several hours every day, the belt-driven type is usually preferred.

Compressor installation

The supply of clean dry air at the proper pressure can be helped or hindered by the location of the compressor air intake. Ideally it should be positioned to obtain the coolest, driest and cleanest air available. Particularly to be avoided are locations near heating pipes, extractor vents and dusty or damp areas.

Spray booths/low-bake ovens

General

Although separate spray booths and low-bake ovens are available, they are normally only economical and practical where there is a very high throughput of vehicles. Most refinishing body shops use combined spray booth/low-bake ovens. A combined spray booth/low-bake oven is a very flexible piece of equipment, but it has the disadvantage that it's not very energy-efficient; the temperature must be raised from the 20 to 25°C used for spraying, to between 60 and 80°C for drying, and must then be lowered back again for the next spraying job. Generally, for most body shops, the increased efficiency offered by a separate spray booth and oven is outweighed by the increased cost, and the more sophisticated job planning required.

A low-bake oven is so-called because the temperature used to dry the paint is normally around 60 to 80°C. This temperature is high enough to cure the paint, but not high enough to damage plastic and rubber components and electrical equipment, etc. The temperatures used to dry paint on a bare bodyshell when the vehicle is built on the production line can be much higher, because there is no risk of damage to trim, electrical equipment, etc.

Specific details of recommended drying temperature and times will be given on the paint technical data/application sheet.

Heating

Low-bake oven come with different methods of heating, but most use either gas or oil-fired burners. The heating may be direct-fired, or indirect-fired; direct-fired heating is more efficient, and the temperature can be controlled very accurately. With a direct-fired heating system, the air is heated directly by the burners, and then circulated inside the spray booth/oven. Indirect-fired heating uses burners which are located in a separate combustion chamber, which passes heat to the circulating air via metal heat exchangers (some heat is lost during the exchange process, which is why this method of heating is less efficient than direct-fired heating).

It's important to note that the heater is not only used for drying paint. Most paints are sprayed at temperatures of 20 to 25°C, and on a cold day, it may be necessary to raise the temperature in the booth to a temperature suitable for spraying.

Some booths are fitted with burners which shut down completely when heating is not required, while others have modulating burners, which react more quickly, giving better control of temperature.

Airflow

The airflow through the spray booth is very important when spraying and drying. When spraying, the airflow carries away overspray and, when drying, the quantity of air flowing has a direct affect on the drying time (see illustration 6.7).

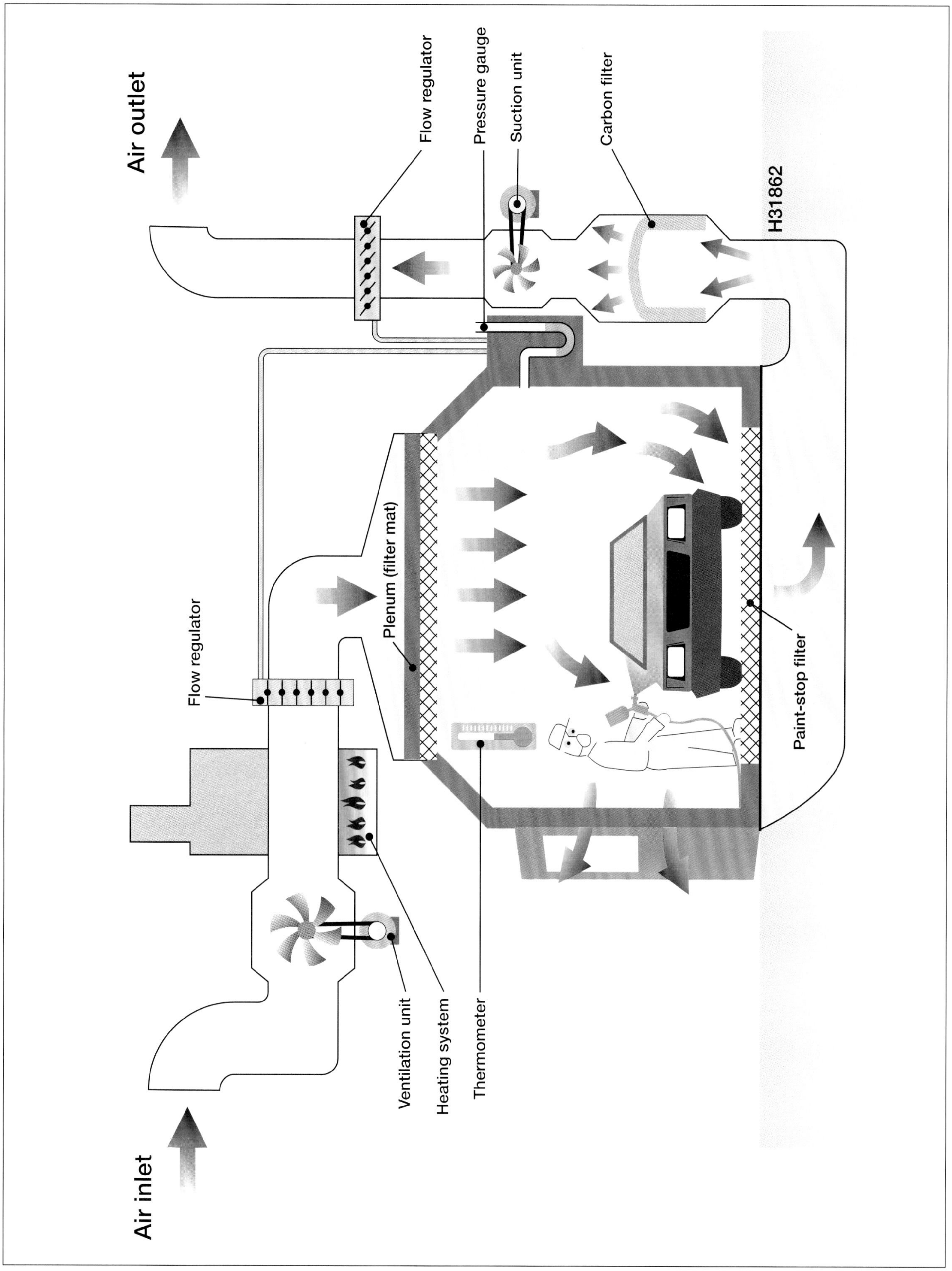

Air outlet

Flow regulator

Pressure gauge

Suction unit

Carbon filter

H31862

Air inlet

Flow regulator

Plenum (filter mat)

Paint-stop filter

Ventilation unit

Heating system

Thermometer

6

6.7 Cross-sectional view of a typical spray booth, showing airflow

There are two basic alternative airflow patterns through a spray booth; downdraught, and crossdraught. Downdraught tends to be the preferred and most common system (and is now required by EPA legislation – see Chapter 4). With a downdraught booth, the air intakes are located in the roof, and the air (and any overspray) is pulled down, and extracted through the floor. With a crossdraught booth, air enters the booth at one end (or side), and is extracted from the other. A crossdraught system has the disadvantage that overspray is pulled forward along the vehicle, rather than down.

When spraying solvent-based paints, a typical airflow rate is around 15 000 cubic metres per hour, which is equivalent to around four complete air changes per minute in an average-sized booth. The current trend is towards higher airflows.

Generally, water-based paints require a much higher airflow rate than solvent-based paints to achieve comparable drying times. Typical airflow rates for water-based paint drying are around 18 000 to 24 000 cubic metres per hour, although this is likely to rise as drying technology improves.

The airflow pattern must be designed so that all areas of the booth are swept by clean, filtered air. Air entering the booth must be filtered to prevent dirt and dust from entering and causing contamination. Air leaving the booth must be filtered and vented to reduce harmful emissions, in accordance with the relevant legislation.

Note that most booths recycle air when in drying mode. This means that when changing from spraying to drying mode, the air in the booth must be purged to remove the solvent vapours produced during spraying, before the air begins to recycle for the drying process.

In the past, spray booths were designed to work under slight positive pressure; ie, the volume of air entering the spray booth was slightly greater than the volume of air being sucked out. This slight excess of pressure was designed to prevent unfiltered air from outside the spray booth from entering and causing contamination (panel joints and doors, etc, are fitted with seals to prevent air from the booth entering the surrounding area). However, in recent years, the ever more stringent Environment Protection Act (EPA) laws in the UK have dictated that negative pressure spray booths are used. According to EPA requirements, the booth must be totally-enclosed, must operate under slight negative pressure, and automatic shut-down of spraying must take place if the booth enters positive pressure operation.

Note that when using a low-bake oven, the drying process begins at the outer surface of the paint, and heat is conducted through the paint layers to the substrate underneath **(see illustration 6.8)**.

Lighting

Good lighting is essential when working in a spray booth. The sprayer must be able to see what's happening in all areas of the booth, and must be

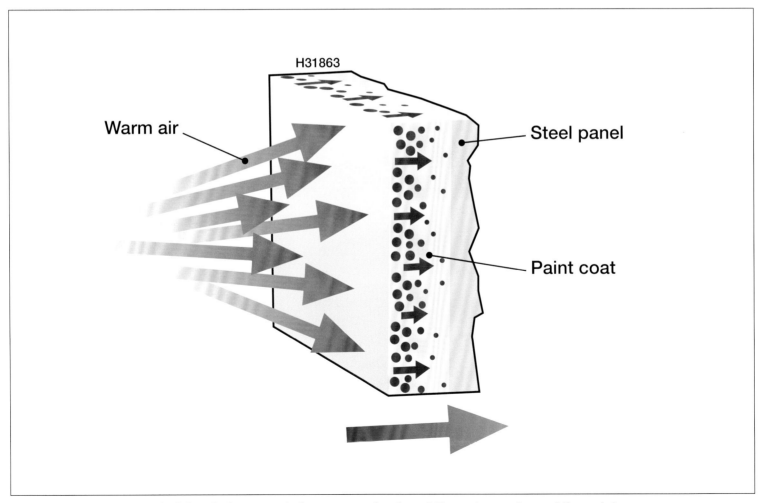

6.8 A low-bake oven drying process begins at the outer surface of the paint

6.9 Typical spray booth/low-bake oven control panel

1 Pressure gauge
2 Over-pressure reset warning light
3 Balance control
4 'Filter change required' warning light
5 Electrical isolator switch
6 LCD display
7 'Burner fault' warning light
8 Burner control
9 Thermostat
10 Lights control
11 Start button
12 Spray/bake control
13 'Number of hours of operation' counter
14 Stop button

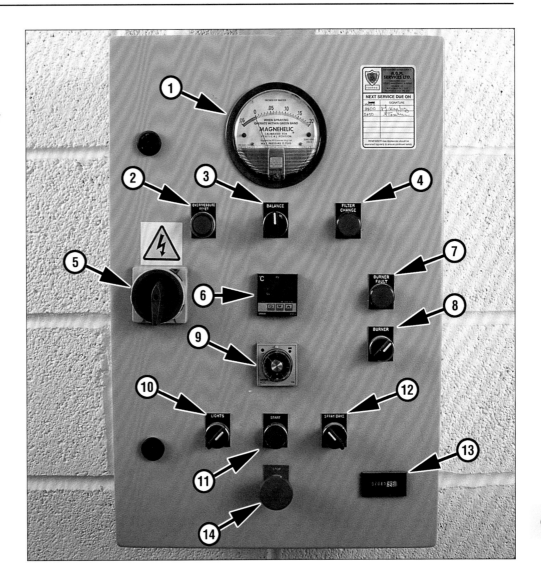

able to judge how well the paint is covering, and whether the newly sprayed colour and finish are consistent with the original finish.

Lighting needs to be even, with a minimum of colour distortion, and must be evenly distributed to avoid shadows. Fluorescent lighting is normally used in spray booths, and colour-corrected tubes may be used to give true representation of colour.

Booth lighting must be designed to avoid 'cross-booth glare'. This occurs when the sprayer is standing on one side of the booth, and has his/her vision impaired by the glare from the lights on the opposite side of the booth.

Controls

The most basic booths have manually-operated changeover switches (which change the booth operation from spraying to drying mode), on/off switches for fans, and a simple thermostat to control temperature. With this basic type of control system, it's important to understand the operating procedure, particularly when changing from spraying to drying mode, and when shutting down the equipment.

Automatic control systems are available, which carry out a range of functions, and help to prevent operating errors. Most automatic systems include a single button to switch from spraying to drying mode **(see illustration 6.9)**. More sophisticated control systems have a self-diagnostic facility to alert the operator to any faults, and to aid fault-finding. Various safety systems are also built into the control systems.

Even when an automatic control system is fitted, it's important to note that few booths are fitted with air cooling systems, and therefore the minimum air temperature inside the booth cannot be lower than the outside air temperature. Because of this, on a warm day it may be necessary to turn off the booth heating to avoid excessive spraying temperatures.

Equipment should always be operated in accordance with the manufacturer's recommendations, and operating and safety instructions should be read thoroughly before using a spray booth/oven for the first time.

Maintenance

All spray booths/low-bake ovens require regular maintenance, and maintenance is usually carried out according to the number of hours of operation.

Intake and outlet air filters must be changed, and additionally, lights, fan units and burner units must be regularly checked and maintained. Always ensure that equipment is maintained in accordance with the manufacturer's maintenance schedule.

6

Infra-red drying lamps

General

Infra-red drying lamps can be used as an alternative to air-drying, or drying in a low-bake oven. The advantage of infra-red lamps is that portable versions are available, and they can be positioned to dry a spot repair, or individual panels, without heating the entire vehicle **(see illustration 6.10)**.

In recent years, there has been a significant increase in the use of infra-red drying systems in spray booths, and the trend is towards systems specifically designed to fit in a spray booth, running on tracks or rails. Some systems are even designed to move automatically over selected areas of a vehicle to assist drying.

Principle of operation

An infra-red drying lamp works using heat transfer by radiation. Radiation is the transfer of heat by waves located in the infra-red portion of the *electromagnetic spectrum*. Because infra-red waves have wavelengths longer than those of visible light waves, they are invisible. When 'heat waves' can be seen rising from a hot road surface, or from the bonnet of a car on a hot day, the effect of radiation is

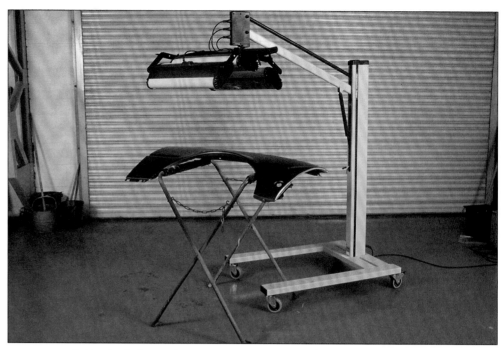

6.10 An infra-red drying lamp in use on a front wing panel

being seen. Similarly, when it feels hot on a sunny day, it's because infra-red waves from the sun are radiating through space and the earth's atmosphere, hitting the body and warming it up.

Drying lamps work by producing

infra-red waves which radiate through the air and the vehicle paint, warming the substrate underneath the paint. This dries the paint by heat transfer from the panel; ie, the drying process starts from the inside, and works out **(see illustration 6.11)**.

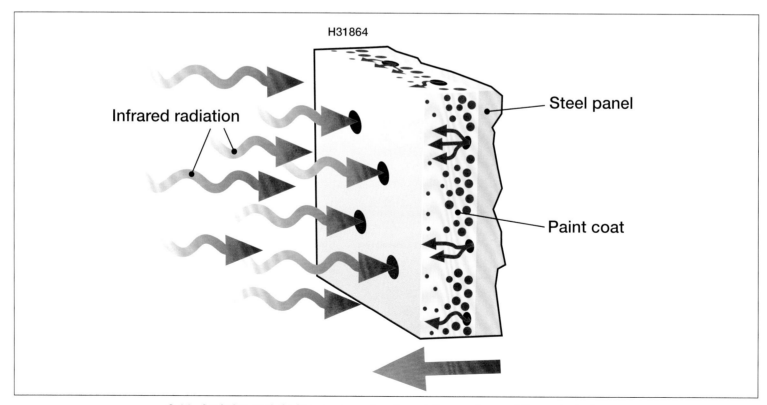

H31864

Infrared radiation

Steel panel

Paint coat

6.11 An infra-red drying process begins at the surface of the substrate

Infra-red drying systems generally give shorter drying times than warm air drying systems. For example, a typical colour coat which has a drying time of 25 minutes in a low-bake oven at a metal temperature of 60°C, may have drying time of around 12 minutes using an infra-red lamp.

There are two types of infra-red drying lamp:

• **Short-wave radiation lamps** generate radiation using quartz tubes. The radiation produced is within the visible spectrum (a red/orange coloured light). Short-wave lamps reach working temperature within a few seconds, and also cool quickly. Drying times are short because the radiation is intense. Short-wave units are growing in popularity, and are gradually superceding medium-wave units.

• **Medium-wave radiation lamps** generate radiation using ceramic plates. In some cases, the radiation produced is outside the visible spectrum, although heat is produced. Medium-wave lamps take a few minutes to reach working temperature, and also take a few minutes to cool. Drying times are longer than with short-wave lamps.

Using infra-red lamps
Refer to Chapter 14.

Sanding and polishing tools

General

There's a large range of sanding and polishing tools available, both hand tools and power tools **(see illustration 6.12)**. Many tools (both hand and power) are designed for use with dust extraction equipment, and this is an essential option when working in a bodyshop environment.

Sanding tools with both rigid and flexible abrasive mounting pads are available. Rigid tools are usually used for heavy sanding, on even surfaces (it's easy to mark a contoured surface using a rigid tool). Flexible tools are usually used for fine sanding work, particularly on contoured surfaces.

There are various different ways of securing abrasive paper to sanding tools, such as clamp fitting, slot fitting, self-adhesive backing, Velcro fastening, or even just manually holding the paper in position when using a small sanding block. Abrasive paper is available in various standard sizes to fit different tools. Paper for use with tools fitted

with dust extraction equipment is usually perforated to enable extraction of the dust.

Polishing tools are used with foam or cloth polishing pads.

Both compressed air-powered and electric sanding/polishing tools are available, and the type of tool used depends on the facilities in the body shop, and personal preference. Generally speaking, air-powered tools have the advantage of being lighter than their electric counterparts, and they are not so prone to getting hot

6

6.12 Sanding an area of filler using a power sander. Note hand tools in foreground

when they have been in use for a long period of time. Power sanding and polishing tools usually run at a fixed speed. Always check the recommended speed for the particular abrasive material being used.

Refer to Chapters 15 and 16 respectively for details of sanding and polishing procedures.

Sanding tools

Hand tools

Hand sanding tools are available as blocks and planes in various sizes, and are used for small sanding jobs and light touch-up work.

Power tools

There are three basic types of power sander; orbital, vibrating, and orbital vibrating.
• *Orbital sander* – the circular abrasive pad moves with a rotary motion **(see illustration 6.13)**.
• *Vibrating sander* – the square or rectangular abrasive pad moves with a to-and-fro vibrating motion **(see illustration 6.14)**.
• *Vibrating orbital sander* – the rotating circular abrasive pad also moves with a to-and-fro vibrating motion **(see illustration 6.15)**. Vibrating orbital sanders are available with various different operating strokes.

Orbital sanders are best-suited to coarse sanding where rapid removal of material is required, such as when removing old layers of paint, preparing panels for the application of filler, and removing rust. Orbital sanders can be difficult to use on uneven surfaces, and tend to create a lot of heat.

Vibrating sanders have a large sanding area, and are ideal for sanding large, flat areas, for example large areas of body filler. Vibrating sanders cannot be used with flexible sanding pads, and are not suitable for use on contoured surfaces.

Vibrating orbital sanders are easy to handle, have good sanding power, and don't develop too much heat. They are suitable for fine sanding work on contoured surfaces, and are ideal for sanding primer prior to spraying colour

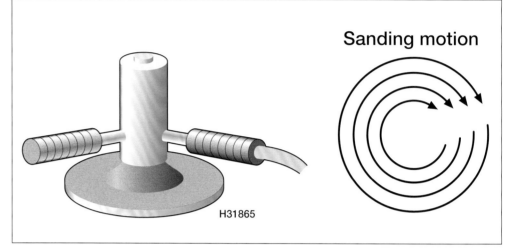

6.13 Orbital sander

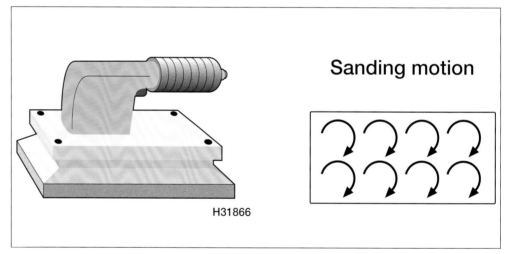

6.14 Vibrating sander

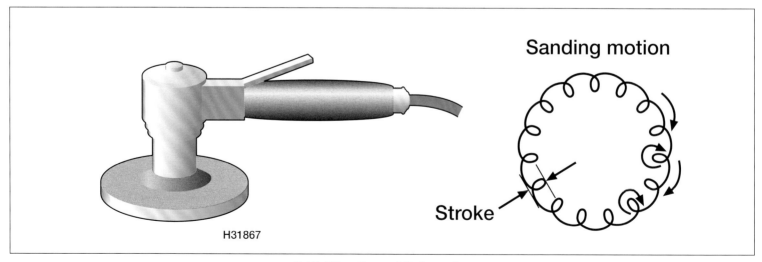

6.15 Vibrating orbital sander

coat. Vibrating orbital sanders are available with various strokes; a longer stroke is suitable for coarser work, such as sanding filler, and a shorter stroke is more suited to fine work, such as sanding primer.

Polishing tools

Power polishing tools (or 'power buffers') are always orbital, and are available with various power ratings and maximum speeds. Generally speaking, a better finish is obtained with higher speeds, but there is also an increased risk of burning the paint due to the increased friction and heat **(see illustration 6.16)**. Always check the recommended speed for the polishing products being used.

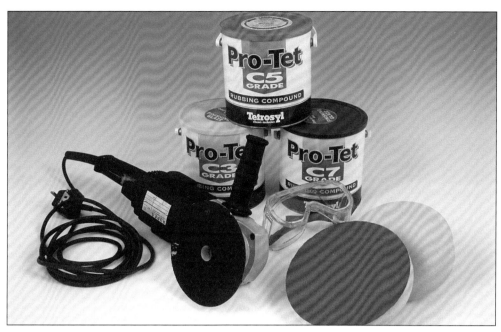

6.16 Power buffer, and associated equipment and materials

Paint mixing equipment

General

When mixing up paint, accuracy is essential, and it's therefore necessary to use certain special equipment, particularly when mixing colour coat. Refer to Chapter 12 for details of matching and mixing paint.

Most body shops will have the following special equipment for mixing paint:

- Tinter rack with built in agitation system.
- Microfiche reader
- Precision electronic scales.
- Mixing vessels.
- Paint mixing rules and/or measuring cups.

Tinter rack

Tinters are normally stored in a rack, which has a built-in paint agitation system **(see illustration 6.17)**. Each tin of paint is fitted with a special lid, which incorporates a handle and a stirring device. An electric motor on the rack drives the agitation system, which rotates the stirring devices in all the paint tins at the same time. Depending on how frequently paint is used, the agitation system may be switched on at regular intervals to ensure that the paint is always thoroughly mixed, and that

6.17 Typical tinter rack

6

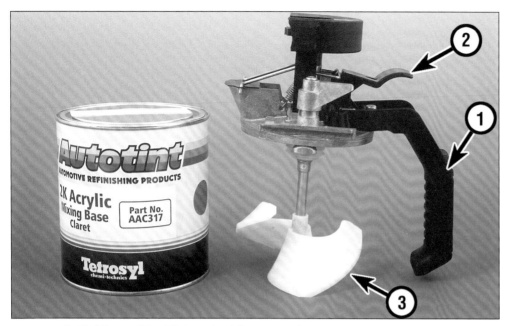

6.18 Tinter lid with handle (1), trigger (2) and stirring device (3)

the paint constituents do not settle out at the bottoms of the tins.

The lids of the paint tins are usually equipped with a trigger to allow paint to be poured easily when mixing (see illustration 6.18).

Microfiche reader

A microfiche reader is required to read the paint mixing formulae which are usually produced by the paint manufacturers in microfiche form (see illustration 6.19).

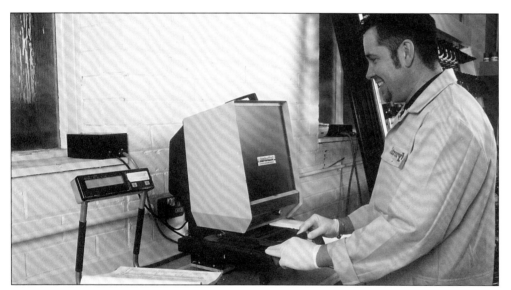

6.19 Using a microfiche reader to check paint formulae

Precision electronic scales

Precision scales are essential when mixing colour coat. Paint manufacturers colour formulae are mixed up according to weights of various tinters. Weights need to be accurate to within tenths of a gram, and inaccurate weights will result in an inaccurate colour match (see illustration 6.20).

Mixing vessels

Mixing vessels must be large enough to hold the required quantity of mixed paint, and must be kept scrupulously clean.

6.20 Using precision scales to weigh paint

Paint mixing rules

Paint mixing rules are produced by the paint manufacturers, and are used when mixing paint, thinner and activator **(see illustration 6.21)**.

Paint, thinner and activator are mixed by percentage volume, and it's important to use the correct mixing rule to give the correct mixing ratios for the particular paint system being used; eg. 1:1, 2:1, 4:1:2, etc **(see illustration 6.22)**.

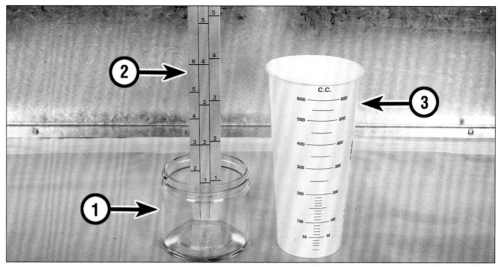

6.21 Paint mixing equipment

1 Mixing vessel   2 Paint mixing rule   3 Paint measuring cup

6

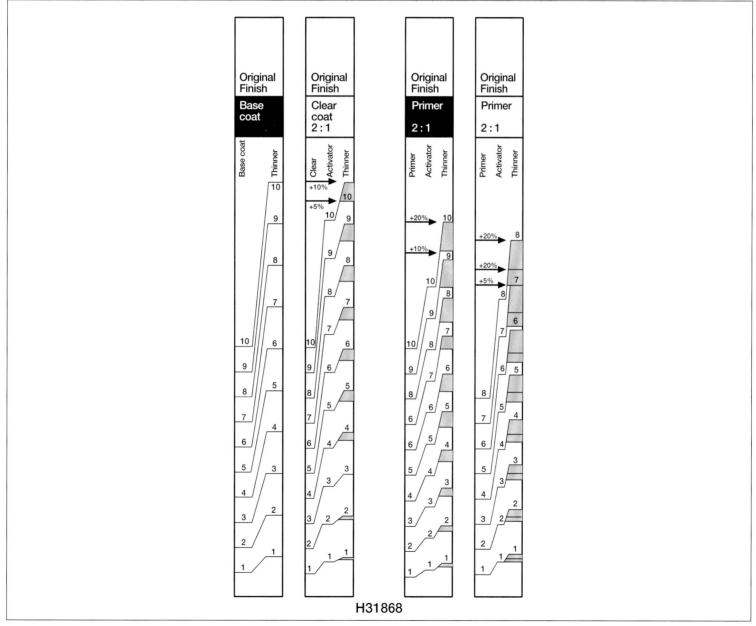

H31868

6.22 Typical paint mixing rules for VAG original paints

6.23 Typical paint manufacturer's colour chips

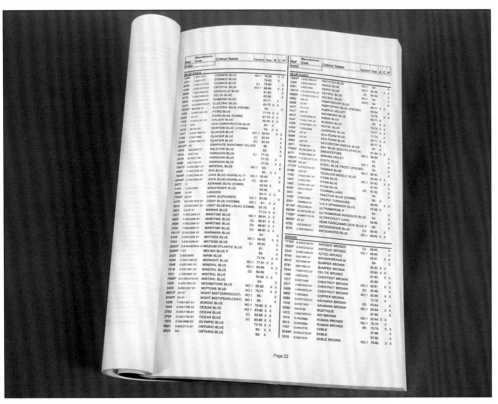

6.24 Typical paint manufacturer's paint code tables

Paint measuring cups

Paint measuring cups perform exactly the same function as mixing rules, except that they double as paint vessels. Paint measuring cups are transparent or translucent so that the level of paint can be viewed accurately.

Colour chart or chips

Paint manufacturers produce colour charts or chips which are used to match the paint colour required for repair work with the existing colour on a vehicle **(see illustration 6.23)**.

Colour charts or chips consist of samples of paint, which can be compared with the paintwork on a vehicle, in order to confirm the particular colour required. Even if the vehicle manufacturer's paint code is known, colour charts or chips should still be used to confirm the colour required; there may be several variations of any given vehicle manufacturer's colour.

Paint code tables

Paint code tables are produced by the paint manufacturers, and allow vehicle manufacturers' paint codes to be matched to a corresponding paint manufacturer's paint codes **(see illustration 6.24)**. The relevant paint manufacturer's paint code can then be looked up in the colour formulation charts, to determine the required mixture of tinters.

Colour formulation charts

Colour formulation charts are normally produced by the paint manufacturers in microfiche form, and give details of the required mixture of tinters to make up a specific colour.

Viscosity measuring equipment

It's normal practice to check paint viscosity before spraying a paint or clear-coat which is mixed with thinner.

This is done using standard viscosity measuring vessels and a stop-watch **(see illustration 6.25)**.

Various standard vessels are available, and the paint technical data/application sheet will give details of the specific type of vessel (cup) to be used for the particular paint being sprayed (eg, 'DIN4' cup, or 'BSB4' cup). A viscosity measuring vessel is funnel-shaped, with a small, calibrated hole in the bottom, through which paint can flow. Each vessel holds a specific quantity of paint.

6.25 Typical paint viscosity measuring vessel

To measure the viscosity of the paint, a finger is held over the hole in the bottom of the vessel, and the vessel is then filled with paint. To check the paint viscosity, the vessel is held over a container, and the finger is removed from the hole just as the stop-watch is started. The time taken (in seconds) for all the paint to drain from the vessel is measured, and this is compared with the specified time given on the paint technical data/application sheet. The longer the draining time, the higher the viscosity.

6

Spray gun cleaning equipment

In the UK, the Environmental Protection Act (EPA) now states that spray gun cleaning and similar operations should be carried out in an automatic, fully-enclosed equipment cleaning machine, or any other equipment cleaning machine that can achieve comparable or lower VOC emissions.

To meet these requirements, most body shops have an automatic cleaning machine for cleaning spray guns. Various different types of machine are available, but most provide a facility for spraying gun cleaner through the gun components under pressure in an enclosed environment. Always operate cleaning equipment in accordance with the manufacturers' recommendations.

Paint technical data/application sheets

For each type of paint produced by a manufacturer, there will be a corresponding paint technical data/application sheet **(see illustration 6.26)**. The technical data/application sheet will provide information about thinning, mixing and drying times, in addition to other information provided to help the sprayer to achieve the best possible finish (eg, spray gun fluid needle, fluid nozzle and air cap sizes, and flatting/sanding recommendations). Recommendations on equipment cleaning, product storage and safety may also be given, although safety data will also be given on a separate Material Safety Data Sheet (MSDS).

The relevant paint technical data/application sheet should always be consulted before mixing up or spraying paint.

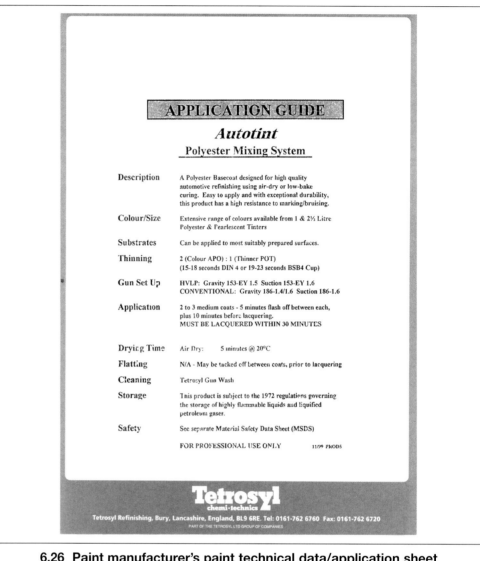

6.26 Paint manufacturer's paint technical data/application sheet

7

Chapter 7
Materials

Contents

Introduction

A vast range of materials and products is available for use in the refinishing industry. This Chapter makes no attempt to provide a comprehensive list, but aims to give details of the most important and most common ones used.

Fillers

Modern body fillers are normally plastic-based, and are designed for filling minor dents and scratches in body panels, to give a good foundation for painting. Generally, fillers are not suitable for filling large holes in bodywork, such as those caused by corrosion. Some fillers are not suitable for use on galvanised panels because their adhesive properties are insufficient to bond to a galvanised surface – it may be possible to apply an epoxy primer to the panel to provide a suitable surface for the application of filler, but it's always preferable to use suitable filler directly on the un-primed panel.

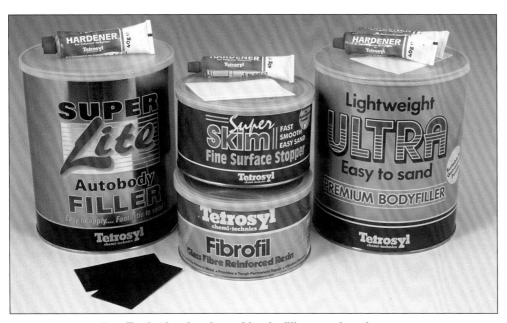

7.1 **Typical selection of body fillers and activators**

Fillers usually consist of two components, the filler itself, and a hardener (also known as activator) **(see illustration 7.1)**. Most fillers use a peroxide hardener. When the filler and hardener are mixed, a chemical reaction takes place, and after a period of time the filler will set hard, producing a surface which can be sanded.

Note that most professional body fillers set more quickly than comparable DIY products.

Refer to Chapter 10 for details of how to use fillers.

Abrasives

General

Abrasives are made from small particles of very hard compounds, which are designed to remove material from a surface via friction. A vast range of different abrasives is available to suit a wide range of uses. Abrasives are usually made up from fine mineral particles, and commonly-used minerals include emery, corundum and carborundum (silicone carbide) **(see illustration 7.2)**.

When a surface is sanded, a hard material is guided with pressure across the surface, penetrating the surface layer, and removing small pieces of material.

Abrasives are divided into different grades, which indicate how coarse (effective) they are. The finer the grade, the less effective the abrasive. For example, a 1500-grade abrasive is very fine, and would be suitable for final sanding of a painted finish before compounding. An 80-grade abrasive is

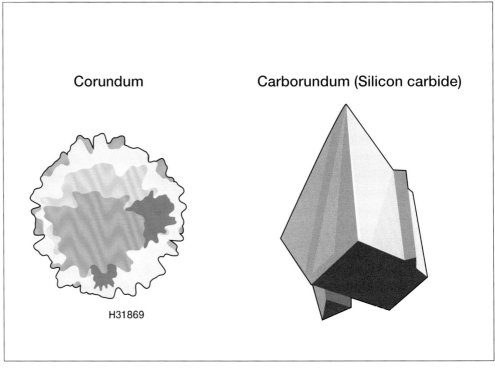

7.2 **Corundum and carborundum (silicone carbide) particle shapes**

very course, and would remove several layers of paint very rapidly, probably scratching the metal underneath (an abrasive this course would be more suitable for sanding hard, bare metal).

Abrasives are available in paper (or cloth) form, or in the form of creams and pastes.

Abrasive papers

Abrasive papers consist of particles of abrasive material bonded to a flat, flexible carrier material. Although products are referred to as abrasive 'papers', the carrier material may not necessarily be paper, and paper, fabric, plastic film or vulcanised fibre may be used as carrier materials (see illustration 7.3).

The most commonly used abrasive minerals on abrasive papers are corundum and carborundum (silicone carbide):

• **Corundum** – is composed mainly of aluminium oxide. In very pure form, it's white in colour, but additives may be used to give a colour anywhere between pink and brown. When corundum is used for sanding, the particles gradually wear and become smooth and dull (see illustration 7.4).

• **Carborundum (silicone carbide)** – is harder and more brittle than

7.3 Abrasive papers are available in many forms for use with power tools and hand tools

corundum, and generally appears black. When carborundum is used for sanding, the pointed particles break off, producing flat-topped particles with pointed edges (see illustration 7.5).

Abrasive papers can be produced with different properties, depending on the application for which they are to be used, and the type of surface to be sanded. The abrasive particles may be arranged on the backing randomly (the

particles are simply poured onto the paper and adhesive during manufacture, using gravity), or the particles may all be aligned (the particles are applied using an electrostatic process). Similarly, the number of particles in a given area of paper can be varied; in a closed-grain structure, the particles are packed tightly together, and in an open-grain structure, space is left between the

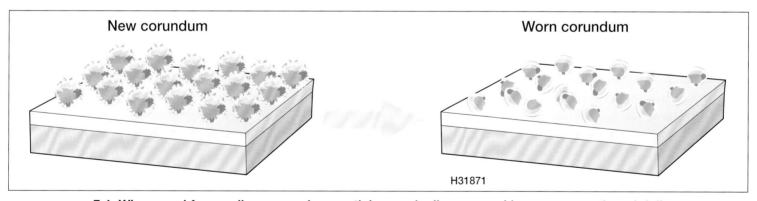

7.4 When used for sanding, corundum particles gradually wear and become smooth and dull

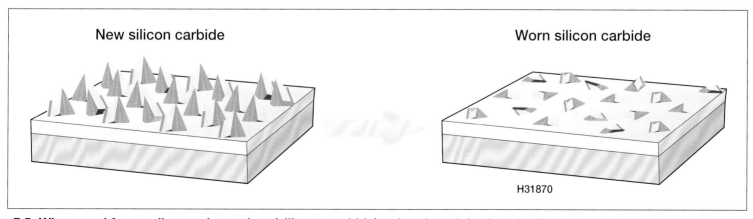

7.5 When used for sanding, carborundum (silicone carbide) pointed particles break off, producing flat-topped particles

particles (this helps to prevent clogging). Sometimes additional additives (such as zinc stearate) may be introduced with the abrasive particles to aid lubrication and reduce clogging of the paper.

Abrasive papers are available in a wide range of grades, and are available for use by hand, or for use with power tools. Papers may be designed for use wet or dry (or either), and are available in sheets, disc and roll form. Sheets and discs for use with sanding tools may be perforated to aid dust extraction.

When abrasive papers are used dry, they are prone to clogging, and it's also possible to generate quite high temperatures due to the friction with the surface being rubbed down. Papers designed for use with water can be cleaned regularly to avoid clogging, and the water will also act as a cooling agent, and as a lubricant when a little detergent is added to it.

Abrasive pads

Abrasive pads may be used for rubbing and flatting work, either on their own, or in conjunction with pastes and creams **(see illustration 7.6)**.

Abrasive pads are usually foam-based, and are only mildly abrasive.

7.6 A selection of abrasive pads, suitable for use with flatting paste

Abrasive (rubbing and flatting) creams and pastes

Abrasive creams and pastes are available in a wide range of grades, but those used for automotive refinishing are generally much finer than the abrasive papers used. Some products are designed to be used by hand, and others are designed for use with power tools, or both. Similarly, products may be designed for use with and/or without water.

The abrasive particles used in creams and pastes are much finer than those found in most papers, and the fact that they are suspended in a paste reduces their harshness.

Refer to *Flatting, rubbing and polishing compounds* later in this Chapter for further details.

Paints and associated materials

Paint constituents

Paints are designed to give protection to the surfaces to which they are applied, and to give an attractive decorative finish. The fundamental principle behind all paints is that they are manufactured, handled, stored, and applied as liquids, which then harden to form a protective solid film of the desired finish.

Paints are made up of three main groups of components; pigments, binders and solvents. Additional additives are normally used to give the paint specific characteristics **(see illustration 7.7)**.

Pigments

Pigments give a paint its colour and opacity, and are responsible for the bulk of the paint. Pigments consist of very fine particles of solid material which are not soluble in the binder. There are two different types of pigments which are used together to give a paint its colour and 'body'. 'Finish' pigments give the paint its colour, and may be used to give the finish special effects (eg, aluminium and mica pigments give metallic and pearlescent effects respectively). 'Extender' pigments affect the paint's 'body' and durability, including factors such as the adhesion properties, and the ease with which the paint can be sanded and compounded when it has cured. Additional special pigments may be used to give the paint certain properties such as protecting the substrate from corrosion.

Most modern paints are 'high solid' paints, which contain increased amounts of pigment to give greater coverage. High solid paints tend to achieve a good quality finish with very few coats when compared with conventional paints.

Binders

Binders are the components which hold the pigments together, and provide the medium for the pigments to flow and bond to a surface, so binders can be considered as the most critical components of the paint. Binders are neither volatile nor solid when the paint has dried, and are often referred to as 'resins'.

The chemical composition of the binder determines the overall properties of the paint, such as the adhesion, elasticity, hardness, weather resistance, and method of drying. Different types of binders are available to suit different applications, and the type of binder used in a paint is indicated by the general paint type; eg, acrylic, polyester, cellulose, etc.

Solvents

Solvents keep the paint in liquid form during manufacture and storage, and they control the viscosity of the paint. The solvents evaporate as part of the drying process after the paint has been applied. No solvents remain in the final coating paint film which bonds to the panels.

If paint is required to be less viscous (or more liquid), it can be thinned using a solvent-based thinner.

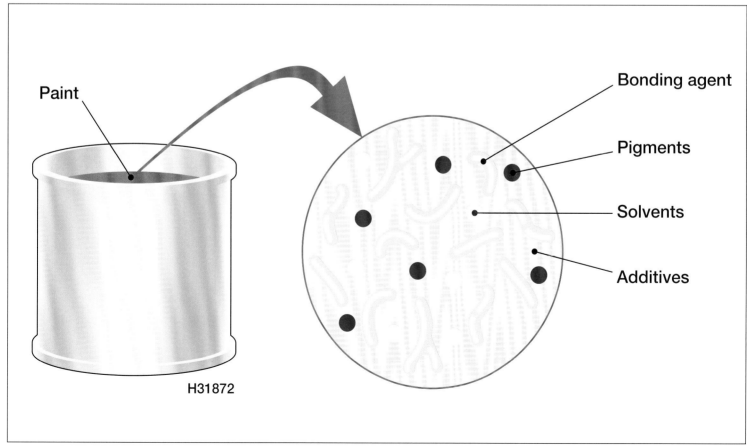

H31872

7.7 The main constituents of paint

7.8 A typical selection of 1-pack and 2-pack paints, thinners and activator

The main paint solvent and thinner do not necessarily have to have the same chemical composition, but both the solvent and the thinner must have a chemical composition which is compatible with the binder.

There are two distinct groups of solvents which are used in automotive paints, and these give rise to two groups of paints:

Solvent-based paints – contain solvents and thinners consisting of Volatile Organic Compounds (VOCs), such as acetone, petroleum products, and butyl acetate. Solvent-based paints are usually stored in metal containers.

Water-based paints – are paints in which water forms the main constituent of the solvent and thinner (the paint still contains some solvent). Water-based paints are normally stored in plastic containers to prevent corrosion problems.

Note that water-based paints are fully compatible with solvent-based paints, and a solvent-based paint can be sprayed over the top of a water-based paint (and *vice versa*) with no adverse effects.

Additives

Various different additives may be used depending on the type and application of the paint. Additives can be used to prevent oxidation, thicken the paint, give the paint a matt appearance, change the way in which the paint flows, and to control various other attributes.

Types of paint

The types of paint used for automotive refinishing work can be broadly divided into two groups. The first group consists of paints which dry through solvent evaporation or by oxidation of the binder (sometimes called 'lacquers' – not to be confused with clear-coat lacquer finishes). The second group consists of paints which dry due to a chemical reaction between two or more elements (often called 'enamels'). Both groups of paint contain solvents, and initially, the solvent contained by the 'lacquers' evaporates in the same way as the 'enamels', but

then a chemical reaction takes place to finish the drying process. The chemical reaction can be triggered in a number of ways, but oxidation, heat, or the presence of a catalyst or activator are the most common. 1-pack acrylic, cellulose and synthetic paints fall into the 'lacquers' group, whilst 2-pack acrylic and 2-pack polyurethane paints fall into the 'enamels' group **(see illustration 7.8)**.

Note that solvent evaporation occurs during the drying of all types of paint, but does not necessarily affect the drying process.

Cellulose paints

Cellulose paints fall into the 1-pack category, and were once the industry standard. Cellulose paints have now been almost entirely superceded for professional use by modern 2-pack alternatives. Although cellulose paint is still widely available for DIY and classic/restoration use, it can be effectively disregarded for professional use on modern vehicles.

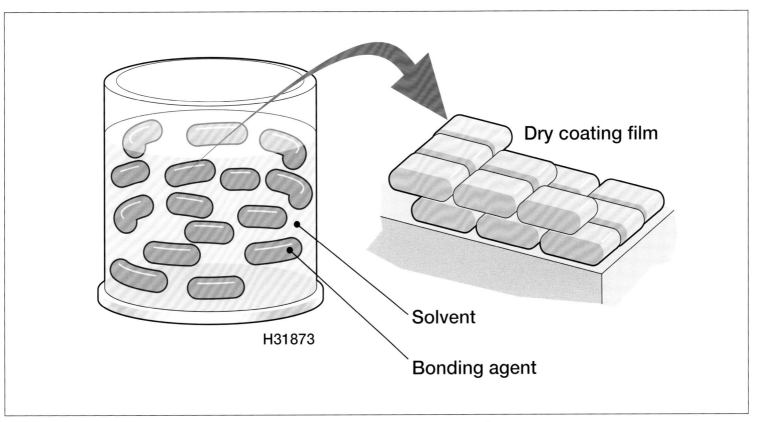

H31873

7.9 1-pack paints dry by solvent evaporation . . .

1-pack paints ('1K', or '1C' paints)

1-pack paints dry by solvent evaporation. Drying by solvent evaporation is the simplest form of drying. The paint dries because the solvent keeps the paint in liquid form, and as the solvent evaporates, the binder in the paint solidifies **(see illustration 7.9)**. Heat accelerates the drying because it speeds up the evaporation of the solvent. Cellulose and 1-pack synthetic paints are good examples of paints which dry through solvent evaporation.

The chemical properties of cured 1-pack paint are the same as those of the liquid paint, and so concentrated solvent will dissolve the cured paint.

Some 1-pack paints dry by oxidation of the binder, in addition to solvent evaporation; as the solvent evaporates, the oxygen in the air reacts with the binder, causing it to solidify **(see illustration 7.10)**.

1-pack synthetic paints tend to be confined to the commercial vehicle spraying industry.

7

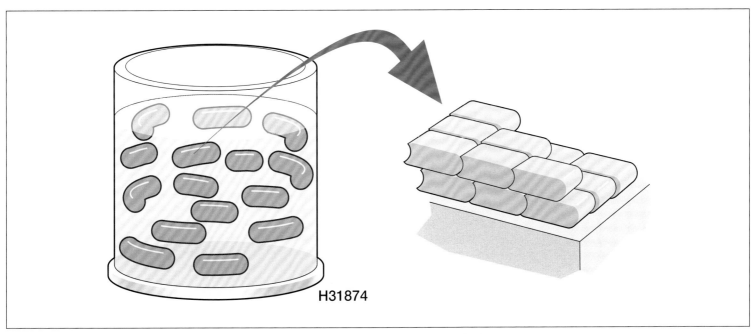

H31874

7.10 . . . or by oxidation of the binder

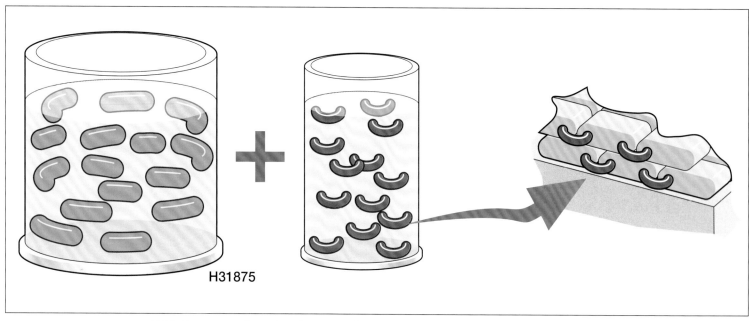

H31875

7.11 2-pack paints dry due to a chemical reaction between two elements

2-pack paints ('2K', or '2C' paints)

2-pack paints derive their name from the fact that two elements must be mixed in order for the paint to cure. 2-pack colour coats and 2-pack clear coats must be mixed with an activator ('hardener' or 'catalyst') liquid before it can be sprayed. Once the colour coat and activator, or clear-coat and activator are mixed, a chemical reaction takes place, and the two liquids eventually form a solid layer through chemical bonding ('polymerisation') **(see illustration 7.11)**. The chemical reaction (curing) can be speeded up by raising the temperature, which is why a low-bake oven or infra-red lamps are usually used during curing.

The chemical properties of the final solid layer are different from those of the two elements, and so the type of solvent used does not affect the properties of the cured paint.

Note that in addition to the base coat or clear-coat and the activator, a third element in the form of thinner is usually added to the mixing formula. The thinner allows the paint to be thinned to give the required viscosity for spraying.

2-pack paints form a very hard finish which is highly resistant to chemical and impact attack.

Etch primers

The purpose of etch primers is to replicate the cataphoretic dip priming process used to protect vehicle panels against corrosion (see Chapter 1). Etch primers contain an acid which etches bare metal, ensuring that there is a very strong bond between the primer and the panel surface. Etch primers are normally used on bare metal, but most types are equally effective on other substrates such as plastic and glass-fibre (check the manufacturer's recommendations as to suitability for non-metallic substrates). Etch primers can also be used on galvanised metal or on top of existing primer to cover any minor damage in the protective galvanising coating.

Etch primers are usually 2-component products, which contain an acid activator. The acid etches the bare metal, allowing the primer to adhere strongly to the panel, and providing excellent corrosion resistance.

Generally, etch primers do not require sanding, and high-build primer is usually sprayed over the top before preparing the panel to receive colour coat.

Etch primers are the only primers suitable for use directly on galvanised panels.

High-build primers ('primer fillers' or 'primer extenders')

High-build primer has three main functions:

• To provide a relatively thick coating which will fill any small imperfections (eg, minor scratches and sanding marks) in the finish underneath.
• To provide an element of stone chip resistance; if a stone penetrates the top-coat, the high-build primer has an element of elasticity to absorb the impact, preventing the chip from penetrating through to the bare substrate.
• To provide a coating which can be sanded to give a smooth, sound base on to which colour coat can be sprayed.

High-build primers are usually 2-pack products which are mixed from 3 elements (primer, activator and thinner).

The term 'high-build' is used by most paint manufacturers to refer to the primer used to prepare a surface for application of colour coat. High-build primer can be mixed with thinner in various ratios to provide coatings of various thicknesses. 'High-build' primer is not necessarily applied to give a thick 'high-build' layer, and can be sprayed to give a thin layer purely to provide a key for colour coat.

Depending on the repair being carried out, high-build primer may be sanded before the application of colour coat, or colour coat may be sprayed directly on top without sanding.

Colour coats ('base coats')

Colour coats may contain various different types of pigments. The pigments used determine the colour

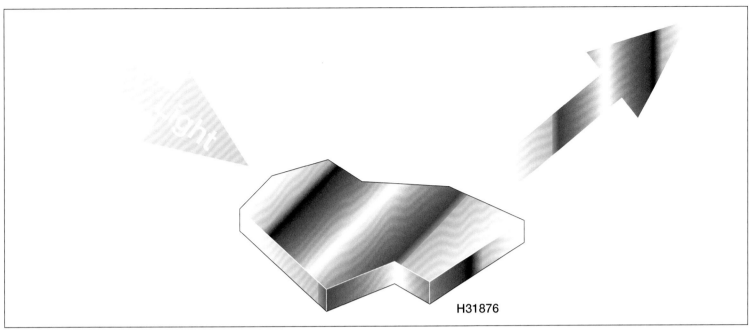

7.12 Metallic pigments reflect light

and the overall effect of the paint finish. The pigments used in colour coats can be divided into three basic groups:

- Colour coat pigments.
- Metallic pigments.
- Pearl-effect pigments.

Base coat pigments

Colour coat pigments are organic or mineral substances which are opaque and colour-fast.

Metallic pigments

Metallic pigments are very fine particles of aluminium **(see illustration 7.12)**. The particles act as tiny mirrors, and give the finish an opaque and metallic quality. The appearance of the finish depends on the number, size and shape of the metallic pigments.

By combining colour coat and metallic pigments, metallic colours can be produced, such as metallic red and blue. If metallic pigments are used alone, silver or metallic grey colours are produced.

Pearl-effect pigments

Pearl-effect pigments are made from synthetic materials, which are coated with oxides of titanium or iron. The oxide coatings and the pigments themselves are transparent, and the thickness of the oxide coating determines the degree of pearl-effect **(see illustration 7.13)**.

When light passes through the

pigments, it's reflected and refracted to give variations in colour.

To ensure that a pearlescent paint layer is fully opaque, the pearl-effect pigments must be mixed with colour coat pigments, otherwise the primer colour will alter the appearance of the pearl-effect paint layer.

Lacquers ('clear-coats')

A lacquer is a transparent clear-coat which is sprayed over the top of a colour coat (solid colour, metallic or pearlescent) to give a high gloss finish. A lacquer is always used with metallic and pearlescent colour coats, and may or may not be used with solid colour coats.

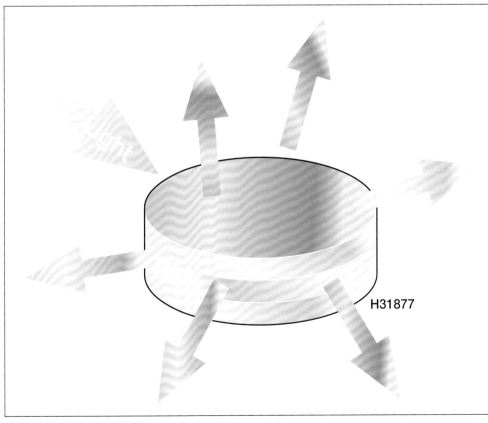

7.13 Pearlescent pigments reflect and refract light

Lacquer coats are sprayed directly onto the colour coat before the colour coat has fully cured. No sanding or compounding need be carried out on the colour coat before the lacquer is applied.

Lacquers are usually 2-pack products.

Tinters

Tinters are the base colours which are mixed together according to the paint manufacturer's specifications to produce a specific colour **(see illustration 7.14)**. Refer to Chapter 12 for more information on matching paint colours and mixing paint.

Once the appropriate tinters have been mixed together, thinner and, in the case of 2-pack paints, activator must be added before the paint can be sprayed.

Thinners

Thinners consist of pure solvent (which is compatible with the solvent used in the paint), and are used to reduce the viscosity of paint to the level required for spraying. The quantity of thinner used controls the viscosity of the paint, and by varying the amount of thinner used, the viscosity of the paint can be varied to suit the ambient temperature and the sprayer's personal preference. Note that with some paint systems, the type of thinner used must be selected according to the working temperature range (eg, in summer, a different thinner may be used to that used in winter).

Thinning recommendations will be given on the paint manufacturer's technical data/application sheet. Refer to Chapter 12 for more information on mixing paint.

Activators ('hardeners' or 'catalysts')

Activators are used with 2-pack paints. When the activator and the paint are mixed together, a chemical reaction takes place, and the paint begins to cure.

The recommended mixing ratio for the paint and the activator will be given on the paint manufacturer's technical data/application sheet. Refer to Chapter 12 for more information on mixing paint.

7.14 Typical rack of tinters

Adhesion promoters

When spaying some types of plastic, if the original primer has been damaged, and new primer is to be sprayed onto bare plastic, it may be necessary to use an adhesion promoter in order to ensure that the new primer adheres to the plastic.

Isolators

An isolator can be used to act as a barrier between two incompatible types of paint. For example, if 2-pack paint is sprayed on top of cellulose paint, the solvent in the 2-pack paint may affect the cellulose paint, causing it to soften.

In practise, situations where isolators are required are rare in the body shop, and a suitable primer is usually used to perform the function of an isolator.

Anti-stone chip paint

Anti-stone chip paint is often applied to vulnerable body panels such as the lower edges of wing panels and doors, and front valances. Anti-stone chip paint may provide a smooth finish, or it may dry with a textured finish, with an effect similar to 'orange peel'.

Anti-stone chip paint provides a thick, rubberised layer, which is resistant to penetration by flying stones and road debris. Colour coat can usually be sprayed over anti-stone chip paint to match the surrounding finish.

Masking materials

The two main materials used for masking work are masking tape, and masking paper **(see illustration 7.15)**. Both of these products are designed specifically for masking automotive paintwork, and alternatives such as parcel tape and newspaper should **never** be used.

Masking tape

Masking tape designed for automotive use has an adhesive which is resistant to the solvents found in paint, and is able to withstand the temperatures reached in low-bake paint ovens. It's also designed to stick evenly to a panel surface, without leaving any residue behind when it's removed. Rolls of masking tape are available in various widths.

Besides conventional masking tape, various types of specialist tape are available for specific purposes.

Fine line masking tape

Fine line masking tape is more flexible, narrower and thinner than standard masking tape, and will follow curves easily without folding and creasing. Fine line tape will give a precise edge (as opposed to the rough edge obtained with normal masking tape), and is useful for masking badges or trim when paint is to be sprayed directly up to their edges.

Foam 'back-masking' tape

Foam back-masking tape can be used for 'back-masking' (also known as 'roll-masking'), which prevents 'hard edges' when spraying up to a masked line. Refer to Chapter 11 for further details.

Masking paper

Masking paper is impregnated with a waxy substance, which absorbs any paint sprayed onto it. This means that masking paper can be sprayed onto without fear of the paint soaking through onto the surfaces underneath. Rolls of masking paper are available in various widths.

Note that good quality masking paper has a different finish on each side, a shiny finish on one side, and a rougher matt finish on the other. Always apply masking paper with the shiny side outwards; ie, with the shiny side facing towards the paint spray.

Plastic sheeting

Large plastic sheets or 'bags' are available to cover the complete vehicle in the spray booth. Once a specific repair area has been masked using tape and paper, a plastic sheet can be used to cover the remainder of the vehicle to prevent any damage from overspray. Some sheets are electrostically-charged so that they stick to the vehicle. Sheets are often supplied in pre-perforated rolls.

Spray-on masking agents

Water-based spray-on masking agents are available, which can be used as an alternative to plastic sheeting when masking large areas. There are several disadvantages to using spray-

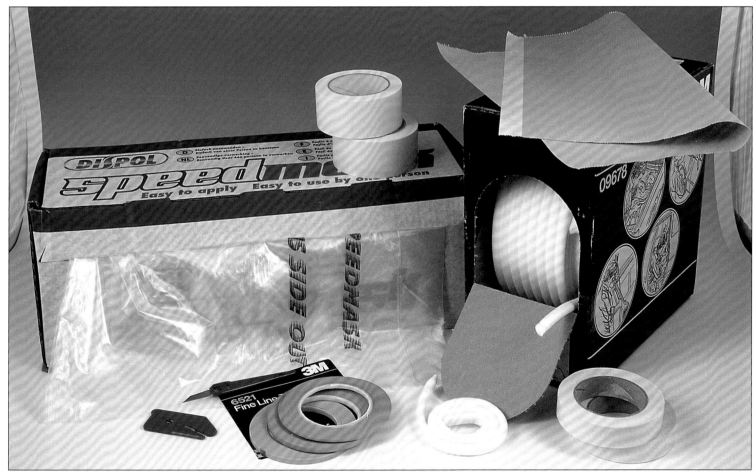

7.15 A selection of masking materials

on agents; they take longer to apply than plastic sheets; a spray gun is used to apply them, which means that the spray gun must be cleaned after application; and spray-on agents must be washed off on completion of paint spraying. These factors all add to the overall job time.

When using spray-on masking agents, the whole vehicle is sprayed with the masking agent, and then left to dry. The masking agent dries to seal the panel surfaces, and retain any dirt and dust. The repair area is then washed with water to remove the masking agent, and the edges of the repair area can be masked using tape and paper in the conventional manner.

Cleaning materials

There is a vast range of cleaning products which can be used during the refinishing process, but they are all designed to remove dirt, dust, and chemical products which are likely to cause problems in the final finish **(see illustration 7.16)**. This Section gives brief details of the most commonly-used products.

Note that cleaning products such as tar remover may be required to remove heavy deposits of tar and insect debris from paintwork when initial pre-cleaning is carried out.

Panel wipe

Note: *Always wear non-absorbent (latex) gloves when using solvent-based panel wipe.*

Panel wipe usually consists of a fast-evaporating solvent, and is designed for cleaning and degreasing work. Panel wipe should be used for degreasing panels prior to sanding (to prevent contaminants such as wax and traffic film from being forced into the substrate), and for cleaning panels immediately before painting. It's therefore advisable to use panel wipe before and after each stage of the refinishing process.

Panel wipe is made from products which should not react with any of the coatings already likely to be on the panel, or which are likely to be used subsequently.

Panel wipe should be applied using a clean lint-free cloth, and wiped off using a second clean cloth. When applying panel wipe to a cloth, pour the liquid from its container onto the cloth; don't be tempted to place the cloth over the container and tip the container up to wet the cloth, as particles from the cloth may then contaminate the rest of the liquid in the container.

It's also possible to obtain cloths which are impregnated with panel wipe.

Tack cloth

Tack cloth is so-called because it is 'tacky' to the touch. Tack cloth is usually supplied in pre-sized sections, on a roll, or in a dispenser. The cloth is impregnated with a resin compound, and is designed to pick up particles of dirt and dust from a panel without

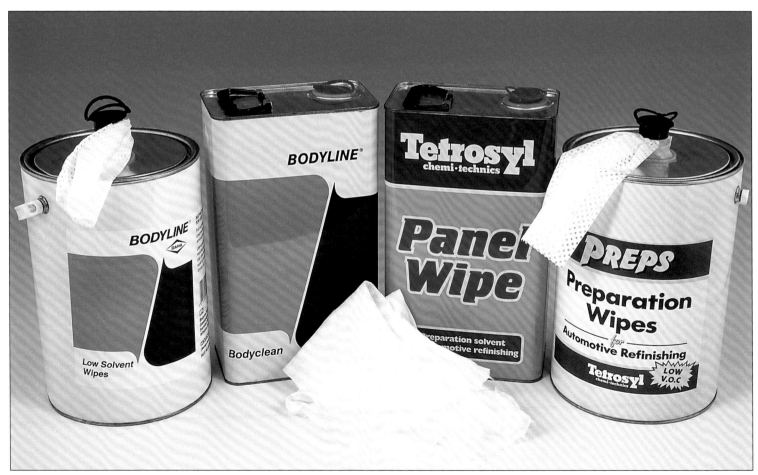

7.16 A selection of cleaning materials

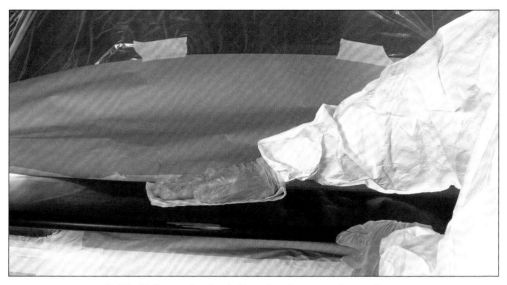

7.17 Using a tack cloth prior to spraying primer

tack cloths are saturated with debris, they will no longer pick up new particles, and may actually spread dirt and dust rather than removing it. Make sure that tack cloths are discarded before they become saturated with contamination.

Spray gun cleaner

Spray gun cleaner is a solvent which is specially formulated for cleaning spray guns. Using spray gun cleaner is far more economical than using paint thinner for cleaning. Note that different formulations of gun cleaner are available for cleaning guns which have been used for spraying water-based and solvent-based paints. Gun cleaner for use with water-based paints usually contains a corrosion inhibitor to prevent internal corrosion of the gun.

It's important to note that most gun cleaners contain VOCs, and are therefore subject to VOC emission regulations. Gun cleaners should be used in purpose-built gun cleaning machines, where possible.

leaving any trace of resin behind on the panel surface.

Tack cloth is generally used as the final step in the cleaning process just before spraying a coat of paint, to remove any small particles which may have settled on the panel surface **(see illustration 7.17)**.

Tack cloths have a limited life span, and the instructions supplied with the packaging should indicate how many times they can be used effectively. Once

Flatting, rubbing and polishing compounds

Flatting, rubbing and polishing compounds are mild abrasives, usually in liquid or paste form, which are used to remove minor imperfections from the final paint finish, and to enhance the final gloss.

These compounds may be designed for use dry, with water, or both. Similarly, compounds may be designed for use by hand or with a polishing machine, or both. Always follow the manufacturers' guidelines when using such compounds.

Note that different manufacturers may use different terminology when referring to flatting, rubbing and polishing compounds. The following is a guide to typical commonly-used products.

Flatting paste

Flatting paste is generally used on existing paintwork to provide a suitable key for the blending of a local repair. For example, flatting paste may be used to flat an existing clear lacquer coat surrounding a local repair, before spraying a fresh lacquer coat over the repair area **(see illustration 7.18)**.

Flatting work is usually carried out by hand, using a cloth or an abrasive pad.

Rubbing compound

Rubbing compound is available in a variety of grades, and is used to

7

7.18 Flatting a lacquer coat using flatting paste with an abrasive pad

remove minor imperfections from a top-coat finish, such as flatting marks, light orange peel, overspray, etc **(see illustration 7.19)**.

Rubbing compound is usually used with a buffing machine, but may be used by hand, depending on the severity of the work being carried out.

Compounding cream

Compounding cream is essentially a very fine version of a rubbing compound. Compounding cream may be used after using rubbing compound to remove very fine scratches, and rubbing ('swirl') marks caused by the rotary action of a polishing machine. Compounding cream can be used to provide a very smooth surface for final polishing.

Wax polish

When carrying out final polishing of the paint finish, non-silicone wax should always be used. Silicone is very difficult

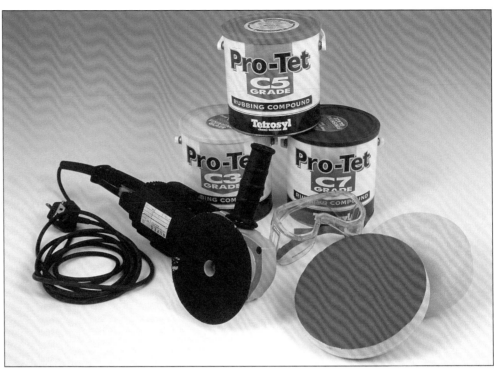

7.19 A selection of rubbing compounds, buffing machine and pads

to remove, and is a constant source of problems when refinishing.

A final polish by hand, using a good

quality wax, will protect the paint and create an impressive high-gloss finish.

Sealants and sound-deadening materials

Sealants

When fitting new panels, or carrying out extensive repairs on existing panels, it may be necessary to use an appropriate sealant to seal panel lines, or even to act as an adhesive to bond panels together. Sealants may also be used on welded panel joints to seal the joints against water ingress and corrosion, and to provide a flexible joint to allow for expansion of the panels.

Sealants are usually supplied in standard cartridges which can be used with a sealant application gun **(see illustration 7.20)**.

Underseal

Underseal is used on a vehicle underbody, and on the insides of wheel arch panels, etc, where unpainted surfaces are exposed to the elements, and to the risk of damage from road debris.

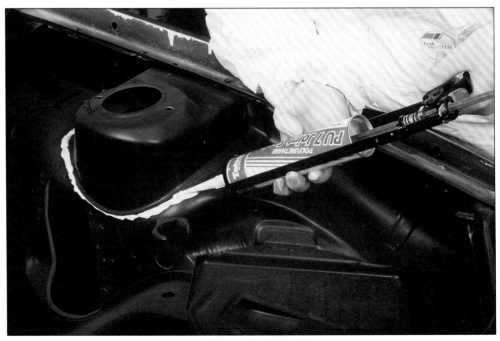

7.20 Applying sealant to a body shell panel joint

Underseal is usually applied using a dedicated spray gun, and produces a tough, rubberised finish, which protects against corrosion and stone chips.

Sound-deadening materials

Sound-deadening materials are used on some panels, such as doors and bonnets, to reduce the level of noise and vibration transmitted to the interior of the car, and to prevent panels resonating. Sound-deadening materials are often supplied in self-adhesive pad form, and can be stuck directly to body panels. Materials are available in several grades, sizes and thicknesses to provide differing levels of sound and vibration insulation.

Some types of sound-deadening pads are coated with adhesive which is cured by the application of heat **(see illustration 7.21)**.

7.21 Using a hot-air gun to cure the adhesive on a sound-deadening pad

7

means that if the fluid tip is changed without changing the fluid needle, the existing needle may not seat correctly in the new fluid tip, possibly allowing fluid to leak through the tip, and causing spraying problems. For this reason, it's good practise to fit a matching fluid needle whenever the fluid tip is changed.

Generally, if the paint type and air pressure remain constant, a larger fluid tip will result in larger paint droplets (more paint) being sprayed, giving a 'wetter' application. Similarly, a smaller fluid tip will result in finer droplets (less paint), giving a 'drier' finish.

As the size of the fluid tip increases, the paint flow also increases (depending on the viscosity of the paint). It's useful to think of paint flow in terms of the speed of paint application required, rather than the quantity of paint sprayed per minute. As a general rule, small panel repairs require a lower speed of paint application, and so a smaller fluid tip (the speed of gun movement over a small panel will be relatively slow). For larger repairs, a higher speed of paint application is desirable to enable overlapping gun passes to be made before the

previous pass begins to dry (or 'flash off'); hence a larger fluid tip may be required.

Another important factor to bear in mind is that if the same fluid tip and gun set-up is used to spray two types of paint with different viscosities, the paint with the higher viscosity will be applied with a thinner film thickness than the paint with the lower viscosity. This means that if the same gun is being used to apply primer and top-coat, the fluid tip may have to be changed to allow for the differing paint viscosities. Again, recommendations will normally be given on the paint manufacturer's technical data/application sheet.

As a general rule, it will be necessary to increase the size of the fluid tip if more paint is required, or if more viscous paint is being used and/or the gun speed needs to be maintained.

Bear in mind that if the fluid tip is changed, the same amount of trigger movement will give a different paint flow rate; ie, if the trigger is pulled to its stop with both fluid tips, without adjusting the fluid control, a higher flow rate will result with the larger fluid tip.

Setting the air pressure

With modern spraying equipment, the trend is towards High Volume Low Pressure (HVLP) spraying techniques, using air pressures at the air cap of around 10 psi, whereas older spraying equipment is designed to work at air pressures of around 50 to 60 psi. HVLP spraying enables more paint to adhere to panels with far less overspray than that produced by high-pressure spraying techniques. The added benefit is that since more paint sticks to the panels, less is wasted through clouds of spray dispersing into the atmosphere, and hence VOC emissions are reduced.

Details of the recommended pressure at which any particular paint should be sprayed will be supplied on the technical data/application sheet supplied with the paint.

Assuming that the spray gun is correctly set up and clean, and that the paint has been mixed and poured into the container on the gun, the next step is to set the compressor to give the correct spraying pressure for the paint being used. An air pressure gauge should ideally be fitted between the air line and the spray gun to enable easy checking of the pressure **(see illustration 8.5)**.

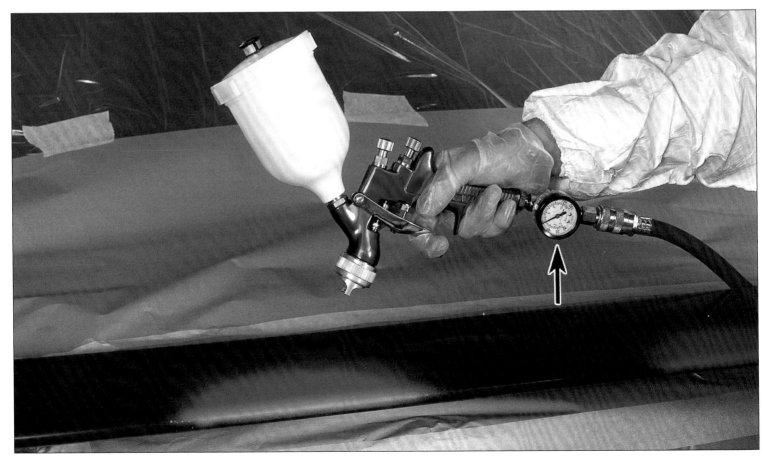

8.5 A gravity spray gun in use. Note pressure gauge (arrowed) fitted between air line and spray gun

Note that some spray guns have a built-in fine air pressure control.

Checking and adjusting the spray pattern

With the spray gun correctly set up, the spray pattern can now be checked.

Once the paint to be sprayed has been mixed and poured into the paint reservoir, the spray pattern should be checked before any spraying is carried out. The shape of the spray pattern is very important for successful spraying, and gives a good indication as to the condition and set up of the spray gun.

Although there are varying opinions on the best initial settings for the air (fan) and fluid adjustment knobs, as a general rule, a good starting point is to turn both knobs fully onto their seats (fully closed), and then to unscrew both knobs fully.

To test the spray pattern, proceed as follows **(see illustration 8.6)**.

a) Hold the spray gun approximately one hand-span (with outstretched fingers and thumb – around 200 mm) away from the test surface being sprayed (cardboard, masking paper, or an old panel for instance), whilst keeping the spray gun stationary, vertical and at right-angles to the surface.
b) Pull the trigger fully for approximately half-a-second. Hold the spray gun perfectly still whilst the trigger is pulled.

The shape of the spray pattern produced will give a good indication as to any adjustments or corrections which must be made before spraying can begin (see *Typical spray patterns*) **(see illustration 8.7)**. Ideally, the pattern should resemble a sausage. Typically, if the spray gun is held one hand-span from the spraying surface, the spray pattern should be one hand-span long. If the shape of the spray pattern is not satisfactory, adjustment or cleaning of the spay gun will be required.

If adjustment is required, turn the fluid adjustment knob clockwise to reduce the quantity of paint, and *vice versa*. Turn the air (fan) adjustment knob clockwise to reduce the air flow, and *vice versa*.

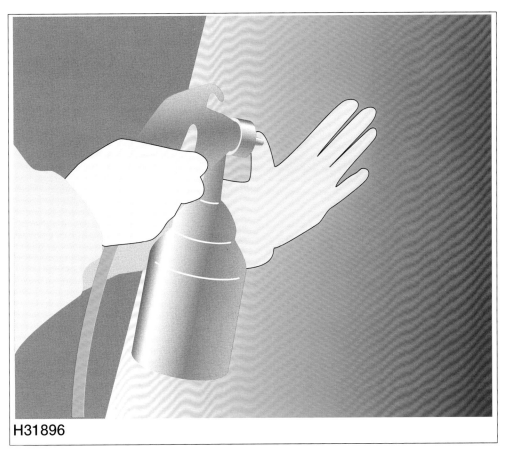

H31896

8.6 Hold the spray gun approximately one hand-span away from the surface when testing the spray pattern

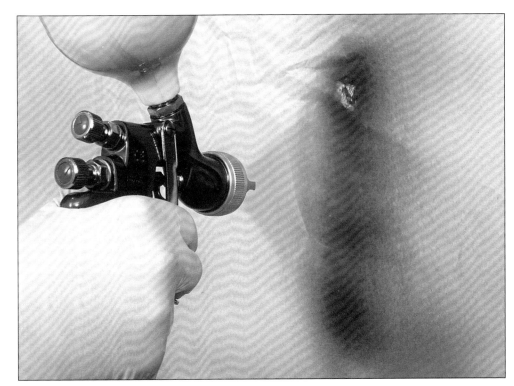

8.7 Testing the spray pattern

8

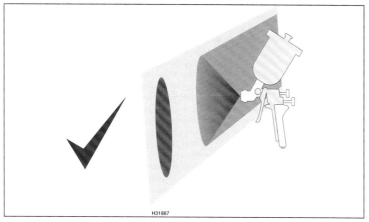

8.8 Normal pattern – ready to spray

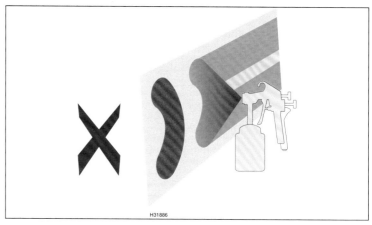

8.9 Banana pattern

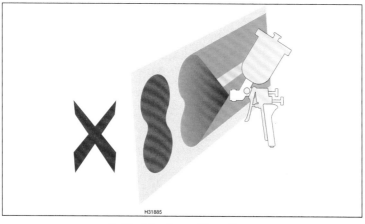

8.10 Single split pattern

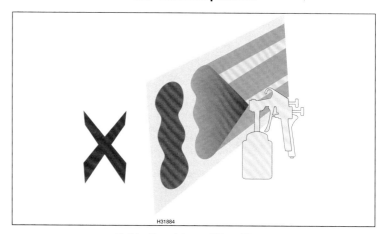

8.11 Double split pattern

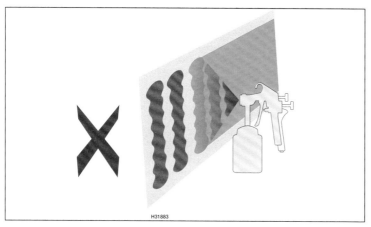

8.12 Intermittent spray pattern or fluttering

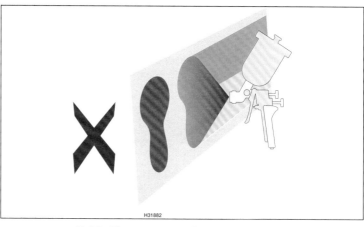

8.13 Heavy top or bottom pattern

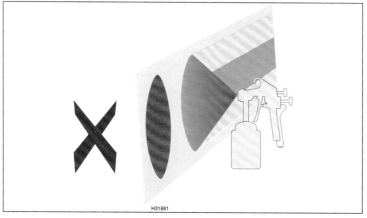

8.14 Centre heavy ellipse

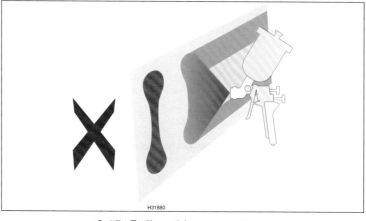

8.15 Ball end heavy pattern

Typical spray patterns

Spray pattern	Fault	Corrective action
Normal pattern	None – ready to spray	None required: • Good balance and uniformity • Symmetrical pattern shape • Good working height and width • Uniform distribution of material
Banana pattern	Air cap horn hole dirty or damaged	Test spray pattern, rotate 180° and test again to isolate faulty air horn hole location Clean air cap thoroughly Replace air cap if necessary
Single split pattern	Too much air for fluid quantity used	Reduce air pressure at regulator Increase fluid flow by changing fluid tip size or opening fluid control knob
Double split pattern	Too much air for fluid quantity used	Reduce air pressure at regulator Increase fluid flow by changing fluid tip size or opening fluid control knob
Intermittent spray fan or fluttering	Air in fluid passageways Insufficient paint in reservoir Fluid tip loose Fluid needle packing or packing screw loose Paint reservoir vent hole clogged	Check spray gun internal seals Refill paint reservoir Tighten fluid tip Adjust fluid needle packing Check vent hole for blockage and clean
Heavy top or bottom pattern	Fluid tip or air cap dirty or damaged	Test spray pattern, rotate 180° and test again to isolate cause Clean fluid tip and air cap thoroughly Replace fluid tip or air cap if necessary
Centre heavy ellipse	Incorrect air or fluid control settings Paint viscosity too high Fluid flow too high Air pressure too low	Check settings and correct Thin paint Reduce fluid flow using fluid control Increase air pressure
Ball end heavy pattern	Fluid flow too high	Change fluid tip for smaller size Reduce flow using fluid control Reduce fan size using air (fan) control

8

Summary

In summary, there are five basic steps to follow when setting up a spray gun:

1   Ensure that the correct fluid tip and air cap are fitted.
2   Set the spray gun air pressure.
3   Fully open the air (fan) control.
4   Fully open the fluid control.
5   Use the air (fan) control to achieve the desired spray pattern.

Spraying technique

Refer to Chapter 13.

Cleaning a spray gun

Warning: Always wear non-absorbent (latex) gloves when working with solvents.

Note: *The following procedure describes manual cleaning of a spray gun, but ideally the relevant components should be removed from the gun, and inserted with the gun into an automatic equipment cleaning machine. EPA legislation (see Chapter 3) states that gun cleaning and similar operations should be carried out in an automatic, fully-enclosed equipment cleaning machine, or any other equipment cleaning machine*

which can achieve comparable or lower emissions.

Once the spraying has been completed, and the paint reservoir on the spray gun has been emptied, the gun must be thoroughly cleaned immediately. Gun cleaning fluids are produced for this purpose, and there is no need to use paint spraying thinners.

Pour a quantity of gun cleaner into the paint reservoir, then swill it around, and pour the waste cleaner into a suitable container ready for disposal.

Wipe out the gun paint reservoir with a clean lint-free cloth to remove all residues of paint and cleaner.

If major cleaning is required, the air cap, fluid tip and fluid needle should be removed from the gun for cleaning (refer to *Servicing a spray gun* for details). Be very careful when removing and cleaning the fluid needle, as it is easily damaged. Additionally, the paint reservoir diaphragm should be removed from the gun and soaked in cleaner.

It's important to make sure that the fluid needle is clean along its entire length – never rub the needle with any form of abrasive, as the slightest distortion to its tip will render it useless.

Check the condition of the paint reservoir diaphragm, which can deteriorate with age. There's a small hole in the diaphragm which must be kept clear for the gun to work **(see illustration 8.16)**. If the hole is blocked, this will cause a vacuum in the paint reservoir, which will prevent the gun from working. There's a corresponding hole in the top of the paint reservoir lid, which must also be kept clear for the same reason. When reassembling the gun, make sure that the hole in the diaphragm is positioned opposite the hole in the paint container lid. If the two holes are aligned, it's possible for paint to leak out of the container when the gun is tilted.

Once the components have been cleaned, reassemble the gun, and pour some more gun cleaner into the paint reservoir. Shake the gun, then operate the trigger to blow the cleaner through until clean cleaner emerges from the nozzle. Once you're satisfied that the gun is clean, dispose of any cleaner left in the paint reservoir, then dry the reservoir with a lint-free cloth. Dry the gun by pulling the trigger to blow air through it.

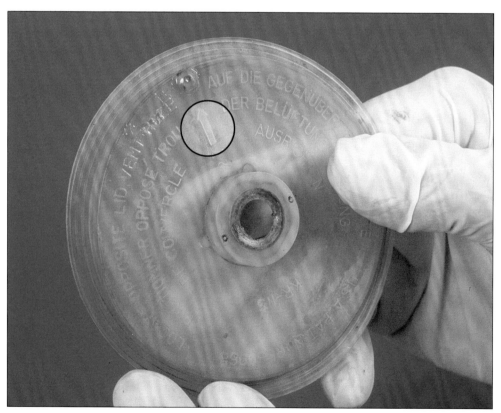

8.16 Check that the hole (arrowed) in the diaphragm is clear

Servicing a spray gun

Note: *The following strip-down and cleaning sequence shows the procedure for the DeVilbiss conventional (non-HVLP) JGA spray gun, but the procedure for most other common spray gun types will be similar. Refer to the spray gun manufacturer's information for specific details.*

General

Spray gun overhaul should be carried out in accordance with the manufacturer's recommendations. Major overhaul is unlikely to be required unless there's been a noticeable deterioration in the performance of the gun.

Dismantling

Note: *For cleaning and minor servicing, proceed as described in steps 1 to 4 inclusive. For major overhaul, follow steps 1 to 10.*

1 Air cap removal

Unscrew the air cap from the front of the spray gun **(see illustration 8.17)**.

2 Fluid needle removal

Unscrew the fluid adjustment knob, and withdraw the adjustment knob and spring, then carefully withdraw the fluid needle. Unscrew the bushing from the gun body using a spanner **(see illustrations 8.18, 8.19 and 8.20)**.

3 Fluid tip removal

Slacken the fluid tip using a spanner or socket, then continue unscrewing the fluid tip by hand. Gently prise off the

8.17 Unscrew the air cap from the front of the spray gun

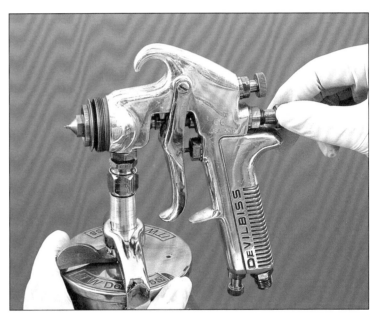

8.18 Unscrew the fluid adjustment knob . . .

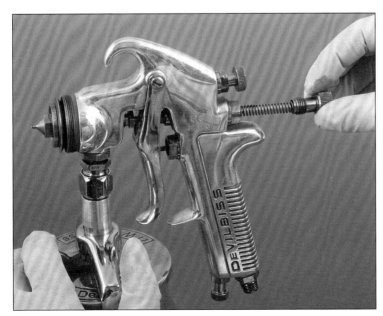

8.19 . . . and withdraw the adjustment knob and spring . . .

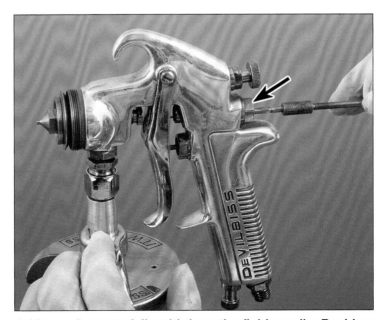

8.20 . . . then carefully withdraw the fluid needle. Bushing arrowed

8

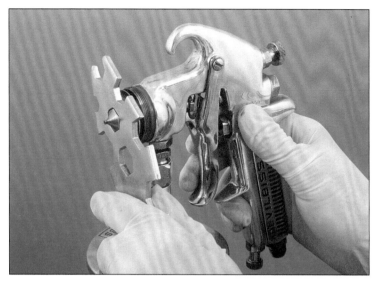

8.21 Slacken the fluid tip using a spanner or socket . . .

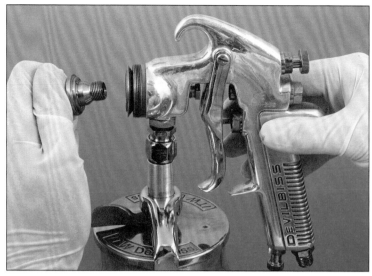

8.22 . . . then continue unscrewing the fluid tip by hand

8.23 Gently prise off the baffle . . .

8.24 . . . and seal to inspect for damage

8.25 Remove the paint reservoir . . .

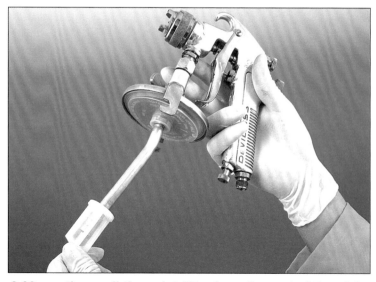

8.26 . . . then pull the paint filter from the end of the pick-up tube . . .

baffle and seal to inspect for damage **(see illustrations 8.21, 8.22, 8.23 and 8.24)**.

4 Paint reservoir and diaphragm removal

Release the securing clip and remove the paint reservoir from the reservoir cover/paint pick-up tube (or unscrew the reservoir as applicable) **(see illustration 8.25)**.

Pull the paint filter from the end of the pick-up tube, then withdraw the diaphragm from the reservoir cover, and slide it down over the paint pick-up tube **(see illustrations 8.26 and 8.27)**.

5 Air (fan) control removal

Slacken the air (fan) control knob bushing, using a spanner, then continue to unscrew the bushing by hand, and

withdraw the bushing and air needle assembly **(see illustrations 8.28, 8.29 and 8.30)**.

6 Fine air pressure control removal (not applicable to HVLP spray guns)

Where applicable, slacken the fine air pressure control knob bushing, using a spanner, then continue to unscrew the bushing by hand, and withdraw the

8.27 ... and withdraw the diaphragm

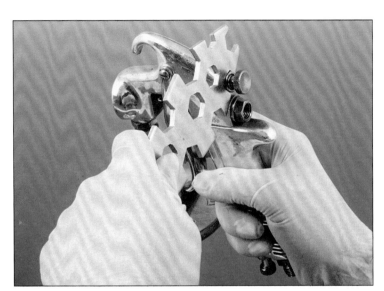

8.28 Slacken the air (fan) control knob using a spanner ...

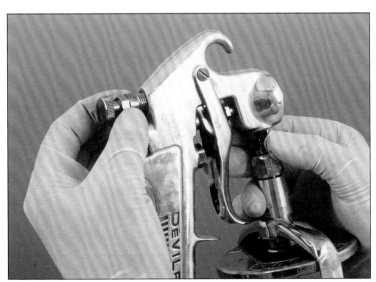

8.29 ... then continue to unscrew the bushing by hand ...

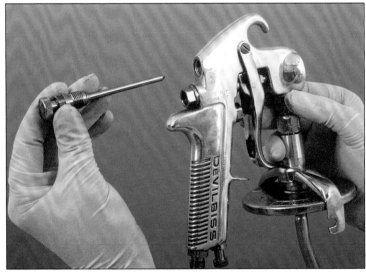

8.30 ... and withdraw the bushing and air needle assembly

8

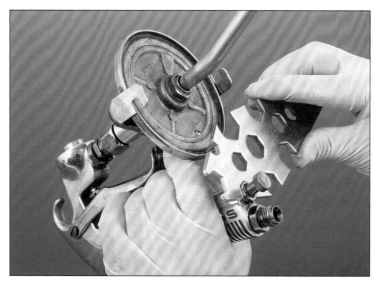

8.31 Slacken the fine air pressure control knob bushing using a spanner . . .

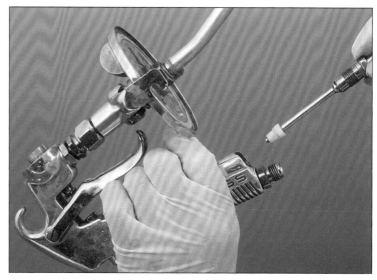

8.32 . . . then withdraw the bushing and air valve assembly

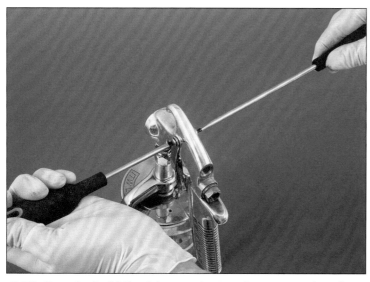

8.33 Counterhold the trigger pivot and unscrew the pivot retaining screw . . .

8.34 . . . then remove the pivot, retaining screw and trigger

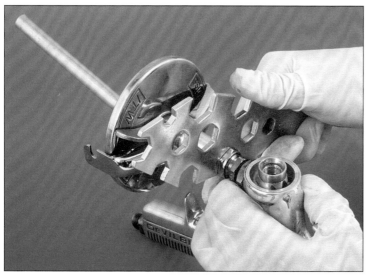

8.35 Unscrew the paint reservoir cover retaining nut . . .

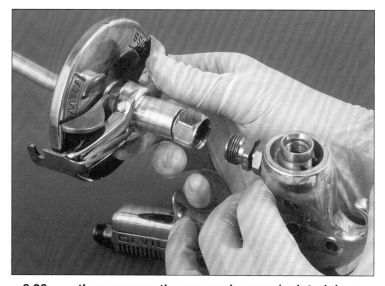

8.36 . . . then remove the reservoir cover/paint pick-up tube

bushing and air pressure valve assembly **(see illustrations 8.31 and 8.32)**.

7 Trigger removal

Using two screwdrivers, counterhold the trigger pivot, and unscrew the pivot retaining screw. Remove the pivot, retaining screw, and the trigger **(see illustrations 8.33 and 8.34)**.

8 Paint reservoir cover/paint pick-up tube removal

Using an open-ended spanner, unscrew the paint reservoir cover retaining nut, then continue to unscrew the nut by hand, and remove the reservoir cover/paint pick-up tube **(see illustrations 8.35 and 8.36)**.

9 Air valve removal

Slacken the air valve using a spanner, then continue to unscrew the air valve by hand. Withdraw the air valve assembly, complete with the spring, from the gun body. Remove the plastic seal ring from the air valve

assembly, then withdraw the control rod/spring assembly from the valve **(see illustrations 8.37, 8.38, 8.39 and 8.40)**.

10 Fluid needle packing piece removal

Using an open-ended spanner, slacking the fluid needle packing piece retaining nut, then unscrew the nut by hand. Carefully lever the packing piece from the gun body, using a small blunt instrument, taking care not to damage

8.37 Slacken the air valve using a spanner . . .

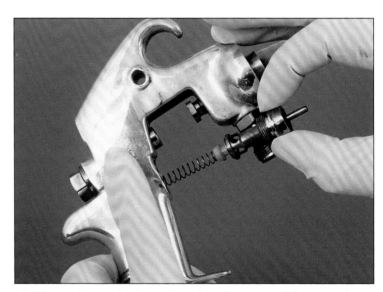

8.38 . . . then withdraw the air valve assembly, complete with spring, from the gun body

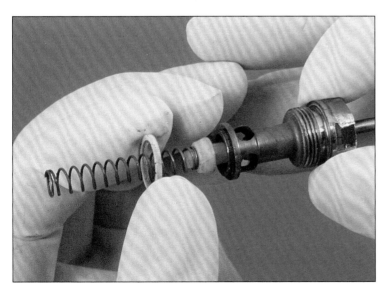

8.39 Remove the plastic seal from the air valve assembly . . .

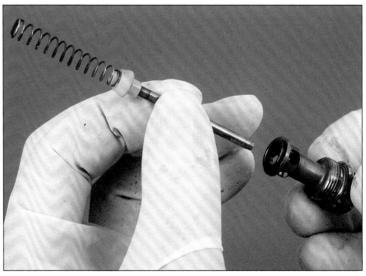

8.40 . . . then withdraw the control rod/spring assembly from the valve

8

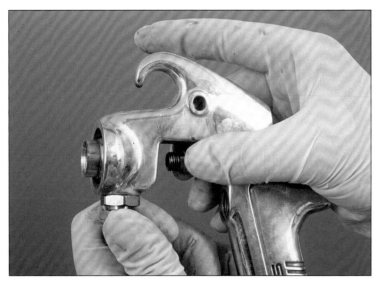

8.41 Unscrew the fluid needle packing piece retaining nut . . .

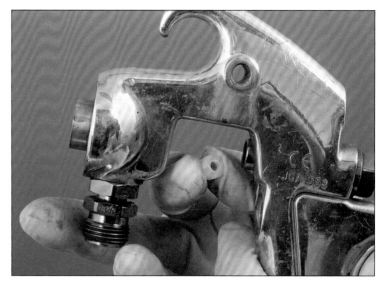

8.42 . . . then carefully lever the packing piece from the gun body

8.43 Clean the paint and air holes in the gun body . . .

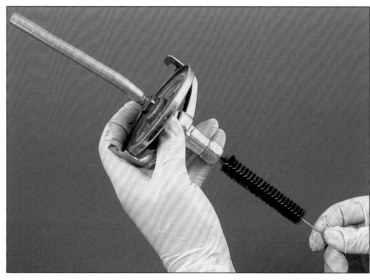

8.44 . . . and the paint pick-up tube, using a brush

8.45 Renew the plastic seal ring at the rear of the air valve as a matter of course

8.46 Lubricate the air valve assembly just below the rear seal

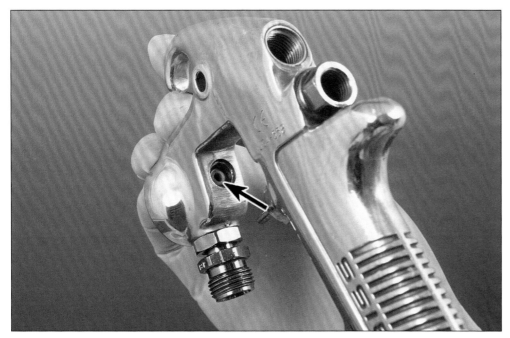

8.47 Fit a new fluid needle packing piece (arrowed), with the wide end facing towards the front of the gun

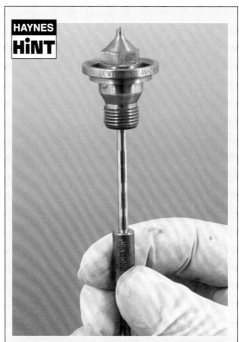

8.48 Hint: Hold the fluid needle vertically, with the tapered end facing upwards, and slip the fluid tip over the end of the needle. Gently shake the needle. There should be very little movement between the fluid tip and the needle; if the fluid tip is loose on the needle, the needle and/or tip are worn, and both components should be renewed.

the surfaces of the gun body **(see illustrations 8.41 and 8.42)**.

Reassembly

Note: *When lubricating spray gun components, always use the manufacturer's recommended gun lubricating oil where possible.* ***Do not use silicone-based oil.***

1 General

With the gun fully dismantled, clean the paint and air holes in the gun body using a suitable brush. Also clean the paint pick-up tube **(see illustrations 8.43 and 8.44)**.

2 Air valve

Check the condition of the valve components, and renew any components which show signs of wear or damage. Check that the valve stem is not bent. Renew the plastic seal ring at the rear of the valve as a matter of course **(see illustration 8.45)**.

On JGA and GFG guns, the wire circlip can be removed from the front of the valve to allow inspection of the front seal. Renew the seal if there are any signs of wear or contamination.

Reassemble the air valve components, renewing the sealing ring(s) where necessary, then lubricate the assembly just below the rear seal

(see illustration 8.46). Screw the assembly into the gun body by hand, then carefully tighten the valve using a spanner.

3 Fluid needle packing piece

Carefully fit a new fluid needle packing piece to the gun body (with the wide end facing towards the front of the gun) **(see illustration 8.47)**. Refit the packing piece retaining nut, and tighten **finger-tight only**.

Warning: Do not fully tighten the nut until the fluid needle is in position.

4 Fluid tip

Soak the fluid tip in gun cleaner, then if necessary clean the hole in the fluid tip using a wooden stick or a brush - **do not** use wire or a metal rod. After inspection and cleaning, blow through the fluid tip using an air line.

Check the condition of the baffle and seal ring. Check the seal ring for cracks, holes and splits, and renew if worn or damaged.

Check the condition of the fluid needle (see step 7) before refitting the fluid tip.

Where necessary, fit a new seal to the rear of the baffle, then refit the baffle to the gun body **(see illustration 8.49)**. Refit the fluid tip, and

tighten gently using a spanner or socket.

5 Fine air pressure control

Note: *Not applicable to HVLP spray guns.*

Check the condition of the rubber O-ring on the control assembly, and

8.49 Fit a new seal to the rear of the baffle

8

renew if necessary **(see illustration 8.50)**. To renew the O-ring it will be necessary to remove the circlip securing the control rod to the bushing. On JGA guns, renew the O-ring as a matter of course. Lubricate the O-ring with a little petroleum jelly before screwing the assembly back into the gun body. Tighten the bushing using a spanner.

6 Air (fan) control

Check the condition of the rubber O-ring on the control assembly, and renew if necessary. To renew the O-ring it will be necessary to remove the circlip securing the air needle to the bushing. Lubricate the O-ring before screwing the assembly back into the gun body **(see illustration 8.51)**. Tighten the bushing using a spanner.

7 Fluid needle

Check the fluid needle for wear and contamination (see Haynes Hint in step 4). Needles which have been in use for some time are prone to suffering from wear rings, which will show up as narrow shiny bands around the needle **(see illustration 8.52)**.

Clean off any paint contamination, but do not use abrasive products, as they are likely to damage the needle **(see illustration 8.53)**. If noticeable wear is found on the needle, the needle and fluid tip should both be renewed.

Inspect the seal on the needle adjustment control bushing, and renew if necessary. Screw the bushing into the gun body, and tighten gently with a spanner.

Carefully slide the fluid needle into the gun.

Lubricate the bushing, then refit the

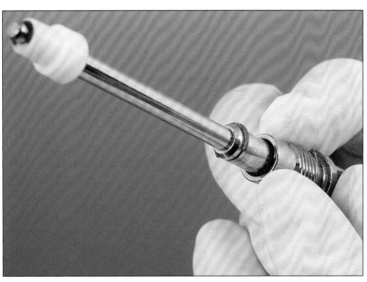

8.50 **Check the condition of the O-ring on the fine air pressure control assembly**

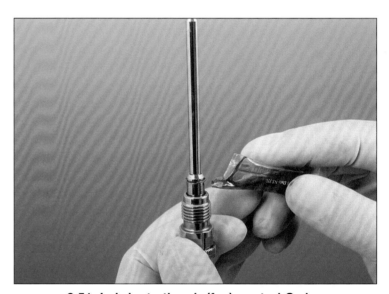

8.51 **Lubricate the air (fan) control O-ring**

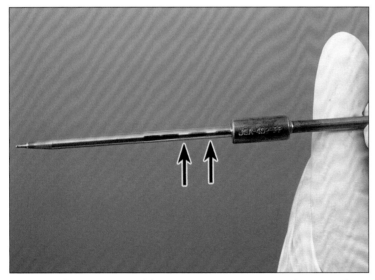

8.52 **Check the fluid needle for wear rings (arrowed)**

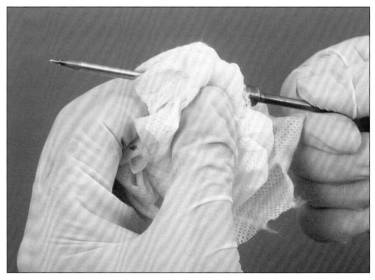

8.53 **Clean any paint contamination from the fluid needle**

adjustment knob, ensuring that the spring is in place **(see illustration 8.54)**.

8 Trigger

Slide the trigger into position, then lubricate the trigger pivot, and refit and tighten the trigger pivot and retaining screw using two screwdrivers, as during removal **(see illustration 8.55)**.

9 Air cap

On some guns, if desired, the air cap itself can be separated from the retaining ring by using long-nosed pliers to remove the clip inside the retaining ring. Soak the air cap in gun cleaner, and clean with a bristle brush.

Check the air holes in the air cap for damage or blockage by holding the air cap up to the light (tilt the air cap at right-angles, as some of the drillings may be at an angle, and may appear to be blocked if viewed with the cap head-on). There are normally four holes in the front of the air cap, and one in each of the air horns. The air holes can be cleaned using a wooden stick or a brush - **do not** use wire or a metal rod. After inspection and cleaning, blow through the air holes using an air line. Also check that the air cap horns are not bent **(see illustrations 8.56 and 8.57)**.

Screw the air cap into position, and tighten securely by hand.

10 Paint reservoir cover/paint pick-up tube

Offer the paint reservoir cover/paint pick-up tube into position, with the pick-up tube angled towards the front of the gun, then tighten the retaining nut securely using a spanner.

11 Paint reservoir and diaphragm

Check the diaphragm for splits, and check that the air hole in the diaphragm

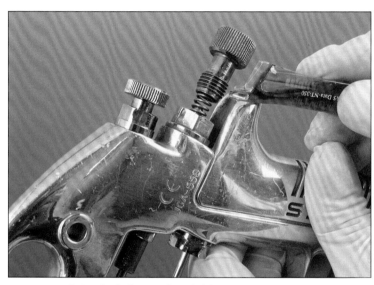

8.54 **Lubricate the fluid needle bushing**

8.55 **Lubricate the trigger pivot**

8

8.56 **Check the air holes (arrowed) in the air cap for damage and blockage**

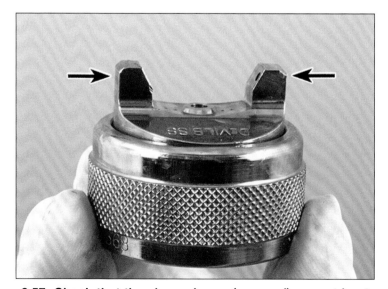

8.57 **Check that the air cap horns (arrowed) are not bent**

is clear. If any damage or wear is evident, renew the diaphragm. If a major gun overhaul is being carried out, renew the diaphragm as a matter of course.

Slide the diaphragm over the paint pick-up tube and position it on the paint reservoir, ensuring that the holes in the diaphragm and reservoir cover are aligned.

Fit a new filter to the end of the paint pick-up tube.

12 Finally

Lubricate the fluid needle by applying one of two drops of spray gun lubricant, just ahead of the packing piece retaining nut.

Pull the trigger and tighten the needle packing piece retaining nut **by hand**. Pull and release the trigger whilst backing off the packing piece retaining nut until the trigger and needle move smoothly.

Spray gun troubleshooting

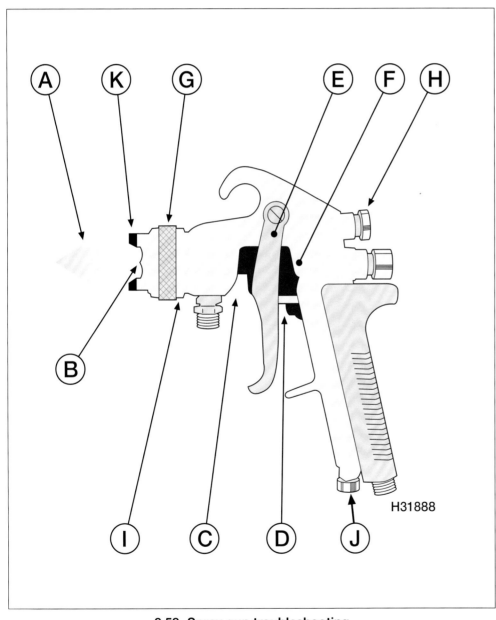

H31888

8.58 Spray gun troubleshooting

The following table gives details of common faults with spray guns, and suggests the possible causes and recommended corrective action. The information applies specifically to De Vilbiss JGA, GFG and GTi guns, but is equally applicable to most other types **(see illustration) 8.58.**

Problem area	Symptom	Possible causes	Corrective action
A	Gun will not spray	No air pressure at gun Fluid needle adjusting screw not open sufficiently Fluid too heavy for suction feed	Check air supply and air lines Open fluid needle adjusting screw Increase fluid pressure at tank Change to correct suction feed air cap Thin fluid, or change to pressure feed
	Gun 'spits' paint when triggered on and off	Incorrect fluid needle fitted to gun Excessive fluid needle wear Excessive fluid tip wear	Check fluid tip/needle recommendations and fit correct item Renew fluid needle Renew fluid tip
	Small air leak from air cap when gun is not triggered	Air valve contaminated and not seating correctly Air valve seal damaged or missing	Remove air valve and thoroughly clean valve, stem and seating Renew air valve seal
	Gun 'spits' paint when triggering on due to paint build-up inside air cap between spraying operations	Fluid tip not fitted correctly in gun head Fluid tip/needle leakage	Check fitting of fluid tip and tighten to correct torque Check for damage or blockage
B	Slow fluid leak from fluid tip and needle seat	Fluid tip internal seat scored, damaged or worn Fluid needle external profile damaged or worn Contamination on needle or fluid tip mating surfaces preventing good seal Incorrect fluid tip for fluid needle fitted to gun Sluggish movement of fluid needle Tight fluid needle packing	Renew fluid tip Renew fluid needle Thoroughly clean needle and fluid tip Check tip/needle recommendations and fit correct item(s) Remove needle and clean or lubricate packing Adjust packing
	Major fluid leak or fluid jetting from fluid tip	Contamination on fluid needle or fluid tip mating surfaces preventing good seal Incorrect fluid tip for fluid needle fitted to gun Fluid needle stuck or 'binding up'	Remove and thoroughly clean fluid tip and needle Check tip/needle recommendations and fit correct item(s) Remove and clean fluid needle shaft Lubricate fluid needle packing Loosen fluid needle packing
	Paint build-up on fluid tip	Fluid tip not fitted correctly in gun head Fluid tip/needle packing worn or loose	Check fitting of fluid tip and tighten to correct torque Check fluid tip and needle packing for adjustment and damage/wear
C	Slow fluid leak from needle packing	Fluid needle packing worn or loose	Tighten or renew fluid needle packing as necessary

8

Problem area	Symptom	Possible causes	Corrective action
D	Air valve sluggish or slow to turn on/off when trigger is pulled/released	Air valve stem bent Contamination on air valve stem	Renew air valve stem Remove and clean air valve stem
	Air leak from around air valve stem	Air valve seal damaged or missing	Renew air valve seal
	Air valve will not operate (air valve stem will not fully slide into valve body) when trigger is pulled	Air valve stem bent Contamination on air valve stem	Renew air valve stem Remove air valve and thoroughly clean components
E	Stiff trigger action	Air valve stem bent Contamination on air valve stem Contamination on trigger bearing screw Contamination on fluid needle shaft Fluid needle packing too tight	Renew air valve stem Remove and clean air valve stem Remove and clean trigger bearing screw Remove and clean fluid needle Loosen fluid needle packing nut
F	Air leak from fluid needle exit point in top of handle	Seal damaged or missing	Renew seal
G	Air cap retaining ring will not rotate	Paint contamination on retaining threads Deformed or damaged retaining ring	Soak gun head in solvent to soften paint Cut retaining ring off of gun (probably renew baffle as well)
H	Unable to turn air (fan) needle adjustment knob on top rear of gun Unable to get round spray	Internal O-ring swollen or broken Paint contamination on threads Fluid tip or air baffle incorrectly fitted Air baffle damaged	Renew O-rings Remove and thoroughly clean air needle Remove fluid tip and air baffle, check components for damage and refit correctly Renew air baffle
K	Paint build-up on air cap	Damaged air cap holes Gradual build-up of spray 'bounce-back' on gun head	Renew air cap Thoroughly clean
I	Air leak from baffle seal	Baffle seal swollen or damaged	Renew baffle seal
J	Unable to turn air pressure control valve on handle of gun (where applicable)	Internal O-ring swollen or broken Paint contamination on threads	Renew O-ring Remove air pressure control valve and thoroughly clean

Chapter 9
Preparing a vehicle for the body shop

Contents

Introduction

In a body shop environment, one of the biggest enemies is dust. No matter what type of work is to be carried out, before the vehicle is allowed into the body shop, it should be thoroughly cleaned to remove all loose dirt and dust (the entire vehicle should be washed, not just the area on which the repair is to be carried out).

If a vehicle is particularly dirty, or it has been used in dusty conditions, steam-cleaning of the underside, wheel arches and engine compartment will help to reduce the possibility of loose debris contaminating the body shop **(see illustration 9.1)**.

9.1 Steam cleaning of the underside, wheel arches and engine compartment will remove loose dirt

9

Pre-washing

The whole vehicle should be pre-washed with detergent and water, and thoroughly dried. **Do not** use wax or silicone-based car wash additives, as this will be extremely difficult to remove, and will hinder the application of paint. Don't forget to hose off the underside of the vehicle (sills, wheel arches, floor pan, etc) to remove mud and loose dirt – this could dry and fall off when the vehicle paint is being dried in a paint oven, creating contamination problems **(see illustrations 9.2 and 9.3)**.

Once the vehicle has been washed and dried, it can be driven (or pushed!) into the body shop for further preparation.

9.2 Wash the whole vehicle . . .

9.3 . . . including the wheel arches and sills

Removing components

Once the whole vehicle has been thoroughly washed, an assessment of the repair area should be made to decide on whether any body or trim components need to be removed. Remove any components which will make the refinishing work easier, and any components which are likely to suffer damage during the work.

Trim and body components

Assess the level of masking which will be required, and remove as much trim as possible, to reduce the complexity of the masking. If items such as badges, lock barrels, door handles, weatherstrips, light units, etc, have to be masked, it can be very time-consuming, and can lead to 'hard edges' in the final finish (see Chapter 11).

The removal of weatherstrips and rubber trim around windows and doors is usually self-explanatory; these items are normally a push-fit, although sometimes plastic or metal clips may be used to secure them. Similarly, plastic trim panels are often secured using clips or screws, or a combination of both.

Trim strips, and items such as badges, are often secured to the panels using adhesive. It may be possible to soften the adhesive by applying heat (from a hair drier or hot-air gun), but in this case, take care not to apply excessive heat which could damage the surrounding finish. It may be possible to use a chemical *releasing agent* to soften the adhesive, but make sure that the releasing agent is not likely to cause damage to the finish, and once the trim has been removed, make sure that the panel is thoroughly cleaned before carrying out any further work.

Some badges (such as vehicle model names or manufacturer's names) may be difficult to remove, and, more importantly, difficult to refit correctly. For example, if a manufacturer's name badge is made up from several individual letters, it can be difficult to achieve the correct alignment between letters when refitting. In this case, it may prove more practical to mask the relevant badge(s) using masking tape.

Ancillary units such as lights are usually secured using screws or nuts and bolts, and removal should be obvious, bearing in mind that fixings are sometimes hidden beneath surrounding trim panels – refer to the relevant vehicle workshop/service and repair manual if necessary for details **(see illustration 9.4)**.

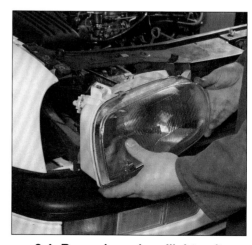

9.4 Removing a headlight unit

Electronic components

If a low-bake oven is to be used for drying a vehicle, consider removing any sensitive electronic components such as engine or ABS electronic control units, which may be affected by the resulting high underbonnet temperatures. Also consider disarming air bag systems where fitted. Refer to the vehicle manufacturer's recommendations for advice.

Air conditioning systems

If a vehicle is fitted with air conditioning, consider having the refrigerant discharged before using a low-bake oven to cure paint. The high temperatures can cause very high pressures in the air conditioning refrigerant lines, which could in the worst case cause seals and connections to leak, or hoses to burst. Air conditioning systems should be discharged by a qualified technician.

Preparing a panel for refinishing

Removing trim securing adhesives

If traces of adhesive are left behind when trim is removed, it should be removed from the panel before carrying out any repair work. Some adhesives can be very difficult to remove, leaving a very sticky residue, and it may be necessary to use a releasing agent or a strong solvent to remove the residue.

Thoroughly clean the panel with panel wipe once any adhesive has been removed.

Removing wax, tar spots and oils

Before attempting to use filler, or spray any paint, the relevant panel(s) must be thoroughly cleaned to remove any wax, tar spots and oils from the surface, as well as any dust.

This is best done using a preparatory panel wipe. Most panel wipes are solvent-based, and should be applied using a clean lint-free cloth. Note that impregnated panel wipe cloths are available, which prevent the contamination problems which sometimes occur when using liquid from a large container. If liquid from a container is being applied to a cloth, pour the liquid onto the cloth. Don't be tempted to place the cloth over the container opening, and then tip the container to soak the cloth – loose particles from the cloth can contaminate the rest of the liquid in the container, and you'll then end up putting dust onto the panel, not taking it off.

Wear latex gloves when using panel wipe, to protect the skin, and also to prevent any greases and moisture from the skin contaminating the panel.

Panel wipe should be wiped on, and then wiped off (always use a clean lint-free cloth). Any solvent left behind will quickly evaporate, leaving a clean, dry panel.

9

Notes

Chapter 10
Using body filler

Contents

Introduction

Fillers are excellent for repairing minor dents and scratches in panels, but it's worth pointing out that fillers are not suitable for disguising or repairing corrosion damage **(see illustration 10.1)**. Most fillers will not adhere to rust (it's almost impossible to remove rust completely), and if a large hole is filled, vibration and flexing can eventually loosen the filler, causing damage to the paint sprayed over it, or even causing the filler to fall out. Even when all rust has apparently been removed, the chances are that air and moisture will be trapped in the rough, corroded surface of the metal when the filler is applied, causing more corrosion over a period of time.

There are two important factors to bear in mind when preparing and using filler. Firstly, filler and hardener are designed to be mixed in a specific ratio, normally around 1 part of hardener to 50 parts of filler. Secondly, filler has a recommended working temperature range.

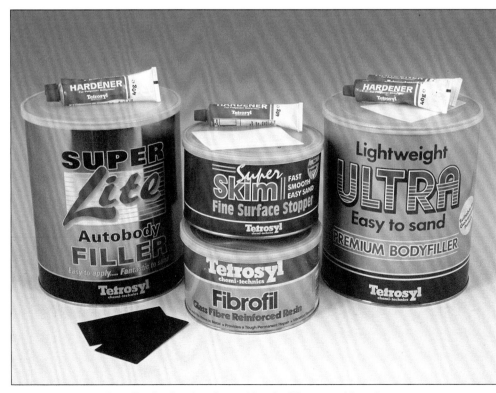

10.1 Typical selection of body fillers and hardeners

If more than the recommended amount of hardener is added to filler, the filler is said to be 'over-activated'. Because the filler and hardener are designed to be mixed in a specific ratio, and a chemical reaction is involved, if too much hardener is added, the excess will not react with the filler, and will be left in the mixture in 'raw' form. This can cause problems at a later date, because the excess hardener can bleed through any layers of paint sprayed on top of it, ruining the finish. When hardener is added to filler, heat is created by the chemical reaction, and if excess hardener is added, the area around the filler may remain warm to the touch for several days, or even weeks in extreme cases.

If the ambient temperature is outside of the filler's recommended working temperature range, the filler is unlikely to cure properly. If the temperature is below the recommended working temperature, the filler may take an excessively long time to cure, and it may be tempting to add more hardener to speed up the curing time; for the reasons already explained, this is not a good idea. Always make sure that filler is mixed and applied within the recommended working temperature range.

Always ensure that the filler is applied and worked into shape before it begins to harden and, once the filler has been applied, observe the recommended curing time before attempting to sand the filler.

Preparing a surface for filling

Any heavy denting should be beaten out (panel beating work is beyond the scope of this book), taking care not to take the surface of the panel above its original height. It's worth pointing out that, generally, fillers are designed to be used with a maximum thickness of about 5 to 6 mm.

Thoroughly clean the affected area, using panel wipe to remove any dirt and polish from the panel.

The best way to assess the damage is to run the palm of the hand (not the fingers) over the panel. This will pick up any minor dents and blemishes. Often, what appeared initially to be minor damage will show up as being more serious when checked in this way **(see illustration 10.2)**.

All paint, and any surface corrosion must now be removed from the affected area, and a reasonable surrounding area. Filler will only adhere effectively to bare metal, so all paint must be removed (if a galvanised panel is being repaired, try not to remove the galvanising layer). This operation can be carried out by hand, but a grinder or power sander will save time. **Do not** use water when sanding down the panel. The object is to develop a smooth, gradual 'ramp' between the material at the base of the damage, and the top surface of the existing good paintwork. Once the paint and any corrosion has been removed, again assess the finish using the palm of the hand, then use panel wipe to remove any residues **(see illustrations 10.3, 10.4 and 10.5)**.

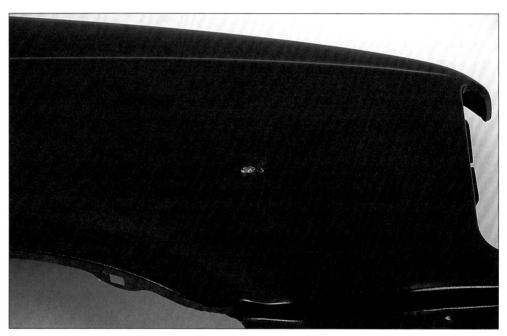

10.2 Typical panel damage which requires the use of body filler on a front wing panel

10.3 Using a power sander to remove the paint around the damaged area . . .

10.4 . . . then assess the sanded finish using the palm of the hand . . .

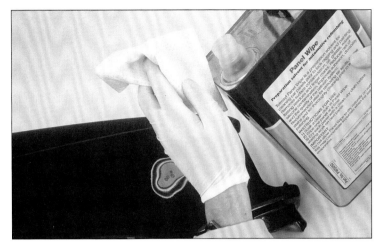

10.5 . . . and use panel wipe to remove any residues

Mixing up filler

If a galvanised panel is to be repaired, make sure that the filler is suitable for use on galvanised metal.

Follow the filler manufacturer's instructions regarding mixing the filler and hardener. Adding extra hardener in an attempt to reduce the curing time of the filler is **not** a good idea, for the reasons already mentioned in the introduction to this Chapter. As a rough guide, a 'golf ball-sized' quantity of filler will require a 'pea-sized' quantity of hardener **(see illustration 10.6)**.

It's best to mix the filler and hardener on a smooth surface such as a clean sheet of metal or plastic – a rough surface (such as cardboard) will tend to allow air to mix in with the filler, which can affect the curing process.

Trapped air bubbles can also make it difficult to produce a smooth surface when working the filler, because the trapped air will tend to cause small cracks and craters when the filler is sanded.

Place the required quantity of filler on the mixing surface, then squeeze out the required quantity of hardener, away from the filler, to avoid contaminating the remainder of the hardener in the tube **(see illustrations 10.7 and 10.8)**.

Once the required amounts of filler and hardener have been measured out and placed onto the mixing surface, scoop up the hardener (ideally with the plastic spreader normally supplied with the filler pack), and place it on top of the filler. Press down on the spreader,

10.6 A 'golf ball-sized' quantity of filler will require a 'pea-sized' quantity of hardener

10

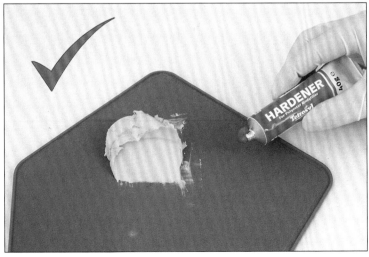

10.7 Place the filler on the mixing surface, then squeeze out the hardener . . .

10.8 . . . DO NOT squeeze out the hardener on top of the filler

10.9 Scoop up the hardener . . .

10.10 . . . and draw the hardener through the filler . . .

10.11 . . . squeezing and folding until an even colour is produced

and draw the hardener through the filler. This will help to force the air out of the mixture.

Carry on folding the mixture into itself and squeezing with the spreader until the filler and hardener are adequately mixed. The filler and hardener are usually different colours which helps when mixing. Carry on mixing until an even colour is produced, with no visible signs of unmixed filler or hardener **(see illustrations 10.9, 10.10 and 10.11)**.

Applying filler

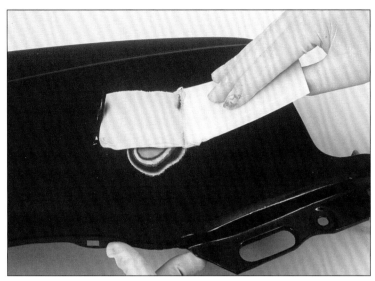

10.12 Use the plastic spreader to press the filler onto the panel . . .

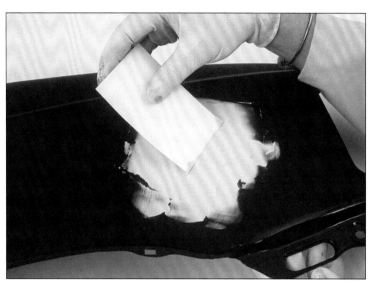

10.13 . . . using a back-and-forth motion

Apply the filler to the cleaned and prepared panel, using the plastic spreader to press the filler onto the panel using a back-and-forth spreading motion (use the same technique as used when mixing the filler and hardener) **(see illustrations 10.12 and 10.13)**. The aim is to end up with a smooth finish, as close as possible to the original shape of the panel (bearing in mind that the top surface of the filler should be slightly higher than the panel to allow for sanding).

Tilt the spreader, and work the filler to give a greater thickness in the centre, and a thinner thickness at the edges **(see illustration 10.14)**.

Try to avoid producing rough edges and spreader marks in the finish, but don't spend too long working the filler, and make sure all spreading and working is finished before the filler begins to cure.

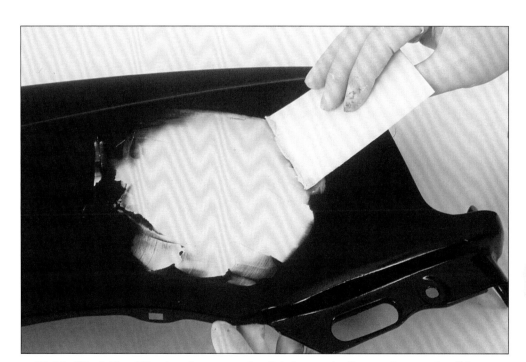

10.14 Work the filler to give a greater thickness in the centre, and a thinner thickness at the edges

10

Sanding filler

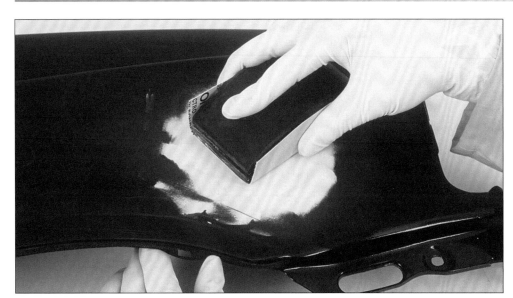

10.15 Sand the filler by hand . . .

10.16 . . . or using a power sander

When the filler has cured (refer to the manufacturer's instructions – usually 10 to 15 minutes for professional products), mask the surrounding paintwork to protect against damage from the abrasives used when sanding the filler. Always use dust extraction equipment when sanding.

Sanding can be done by hand (always use a sanding block - if sanding is carried out by holding the abrasive paper directly by hand, it will almost certainly produce an uneven surface), or using a power sander **(see illustrations 10.15 and 10.16)**. The filler manufacturer will usually provide recommendations for the grades of abrasives to be used when sanding; if not, it should be safe to start with 80-grade paper. **Never** use water when sanding down filler, as the filler will absorb water; even if the surface is dried immediately, moisture absorbed deep into the filler may come to the surface after a few weeks, causing pinhead bubbles in the paint sprayed over the top.

As sanding progresses, and a smooth finish is obtained, it will be necessary to identify any low spots in the surface of the filler. This can be done using a 'dry guide coat' which consists of a layer of dry graphite powder which is brushed onto the panel surface. The excess powder is then wiped off, and any powder left behind indicates low spots in the filler surface which may require further filling. The same effect can be achieved by spraying a coat of dark, matt colour over the repair area,

10.17 Apply a dry guide coat to identify any low spots in the filler

10.18 Alternatively, spray a coat of dark, matt colour . . .

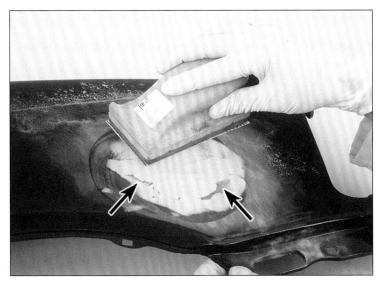

10.19 . . . and sand lightly to identify any low spots

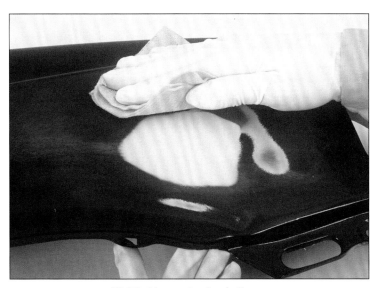

10.20 Use a tack cloth . . .

and then sanding lightly. Again, any areas of colour left behind indicate low spots **(see illustrations 10.17, 10.18 and 10.19)**.

Remove all the sanding dust from the repaired area, using a clean dry cloth followed by a tack cloth, then if necessary add more filler to fill any low spots **(see illustrations 10.20 and 10.21)**.

Repeat the sanding procedure, and check again for low spots, then continue sanding using around 180-grade to 240-grade abrasive. The object at this stage is to shape the filler to a point where it's flat, and blends in

with the surrounding panel surfaces.

Even when using dust-extraction equipment, use a tack cloth to remove dust regularly during the sanding process, otherwise the dust may fill and hide fine imperfections in the finish.

Check for smoothness of the finish using the palm of the hand, as described previously. If necessary, repeat the filling and sanding process until the filler blends in with the surrounding surfaces of the panel, with no high or low spots. Some damage will require two or even three layers of filler.

Finish sanding, by hand, using around 320-grade abrasive to remove

sanding scratches and minor imperfections, and to give a smooth texture. Make sure that all sanding scratches in the filler and surrounding panel are removed – paint (even primer) won't cover sanding scratches.

Once you're satisfied with the finish of the repaired area, the repair should be sprayed with etch primer as soon as possible, and certainly before the vehicle is taken outside **(see illustration 10.22)**. If no paint is applied, any moisture in the air may be absorbed by the filler, which can cause problems with the finish at a later date.

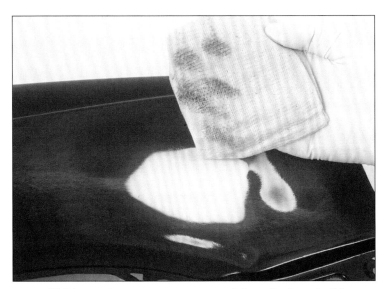

10.21 . . . to remove any remaining dust and dirt

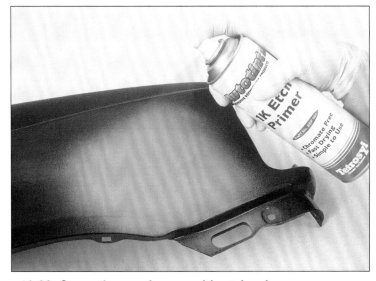

10.22 Spray the repair area with etch primer as soon as possible

10

Notes

Notes

Chapter 11
Masking

Contents

Introduction

Masking is an essential part of the preparation for paint spraying **(see illustration 11.1)**. The purpose of masking is to prevent unwanted paint overspray onto surrounding panels and trim. Overspray will give an obvious indication that spraying work has been carried out, no matter how professional the final finish, and it can be very difficult and time-consuming to remove.

When a spray gun is used in a spray booth, a fine mist of paint is produced over a much wider area than the area being sprayed, and it's very easy to underestimate the amount of masking required. If meticulous masking is not carried out, the overspray can ruin a previously perfectly good finish. Minor overspray on the body panels can be cleaned off or even sprayed over, but trim pieces, badges, etc, can be very difficult to clean effectively.

Take care not to underestimate the amount of masking required. It's

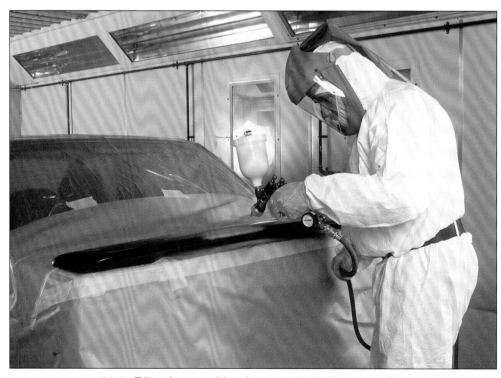

11.1 Effective masking is essential when spraying

standard practise to cover the whole vehicle (with the exception of the repair area) with a plastic sheet to prevent overspray when carrying out a repair.

Poor masking can produce 'hard edges' between newly sprayed paint and the original paintwork; again, this can be difficult and time-consuming to cure.

When planning a refinishing job, it's always important to allow enough time for effective masking.

Different people have different opinions on the best way to go about masking, but the following will serve as a guide.

Before masking, the panels to be masked should be thoroughly cleaned using panel wipe. This will remove any surface contamination, and will reduce the static which attracts dust. Remember not to use water to clean any areas where filler has been applied.

Ensure that the panels are thoroughly dry before beginning the masking process.

Masking materials

Refer to *Masking materials* in Chapter 7 for details.

Removing trim and bodywork fittings

Before masking, it's preferable to remove as much trim as possible, to reduce the complexity of the masking required. If items such as badges, lock barrels, door handles, weatherstrips, light units, etc, have to be masked, it can be very time-consuming, and can lead to 'hard edges' in the final finish. A 'hard edge' is one of the worst and most noticeable mistakes which can be made during spraying.

Some badges (such as vehicle model names or manufacturer's names) may be difficult to remove, and, more importantly, difficult to refit correctly. For example, if a manufacturer's name badge is made up from several individual letters, it can be difficult to achieve the correct alignment between letters when refitting. In this case, it may prove more practical to mask the relevant badge(s) using masking tape.

Refer to Chapter 9 for brief details of removing trim.

General masking technique

11.2 Withdrawing taped masking paper from a masking paper dispenser

Masking paper dispensers

Most body shops have masking paper dispensers, which hold a roll of masking paper and a roll of tape, and provide a source of masking paper with masking tape already stuck to one edge **(see illustration 11.2)**. This simplifies the masking process, and helps to avoid creases along the edge of the paper.

Applying masking tape

To make life easier, when masking up to the edge of a repair area, mask the edge of the area using a strip of tape first, then secure masking paper with extra tape, overlapping the tape used to mask the edge **(see illustrations 11.3 and 11.4)**.

When applying masking tape directly from a roll, don't pull a long length of tape from the roll and then attempt to stick it into position. The best method is to unroll a short length

11.3 Mask the edge of the repair area using masking tape . . .

11.4 . . . then secure masking paper with extra tape

of tape and to stick this in position. The roll of tape can then be manoeuvred and unrolled with one hand, while the other hand is used to place and secure the tape. This will help to prevent creases in the tape, and will allow more accurate positioning.

'Fine line' masking tape

'Fine line' tape is more flexible, narrower and thinner than standard masking tape, and will follow curves easily without folding and creasing. Fine line tape will give a precise edge (as opposed to the rough edge obtained with normal masking tape), and is useful for masking badges or trim when paint is to be sprayed directly up to their edges.

When masking trim, or masking along the edge of curved body panels, it's not always easy to lay a smooth run of standard masking tape, as the tape will tend to fold and crease, instead of flowing smoothly around contours. When masking around contours, it's often easiest to use fine line masking tape. Fine line tape should only be used for masking the edge of a panel or a piece of trim adjacent to an area which is due to be sprayed; additional strips of standard masking tape and paper can then be stuck to overlap the edge of the fine line tape **(see illustration 11.5)**.

Fine line masking tape is also useful when masking right-angled corners. If care is taken, the tape can be bent

around the corner, which is preferable to using two pieces of standard tape and then trimming with a knife **(see illustration 11.6)**.

Applying masking paper

Note that good quality masking paper has a different finish on each side, a shiny finish on one side, and a rougher matt finish on the other. Always apply masking paper with the shiny side outwards; ie, with the shiny side facing towards the paint spray.

Whenever masking is carried out, always remember that paint will cover everything that it touches. Even small slits between masking tape and paper will allow paint to cover the surface exposed between them. If masking

11

11.5 Using fine line masking tape to mask around the edge of a curved trim panel

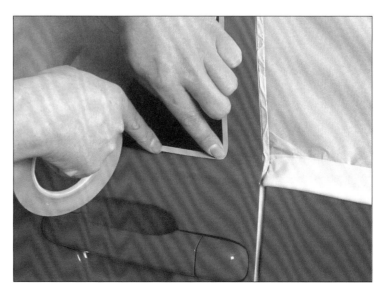

11.6 Masking around the edge of a window using fine line masking tape

11.7 Run tape along the full length of masking paper edges

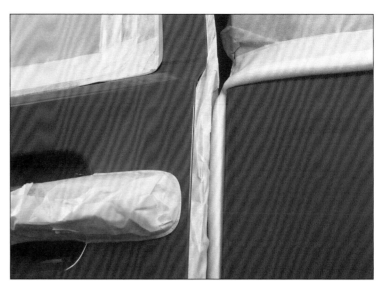

11.8 Masked door handle assembly

paper edges are not adequately secured, they will blow open during spraying work, and allow mists of overspray to reach the spaces beneath the paper. To avoid these problems, always run tape along the full length of paper edges to completely seal off the surfaces underneath. This is particularly important when the edge of one sheet of masking paper is overlapped with another **(see illustration 11.7)**.

When overlapping sheets of masking paper, it's good practise to make sure that the overlaps face away from the direction of paint spray; ie, ensure that the sheet of paper nearest to the paint spray is positioned on top of any adjoining sheets. This will avoid any raised edges at the overlap, which may cause turbulence, deflecting the paint spray and disturbing dust.

One of the keys to successful masking is to keep the masking material as smooth and crease-free as possible. If masking paper is applied so that it's loose and creased, the flow of air and paint from the spray gun will ruffle the paper, which could affect the spray pattern and disturb any dust present.

When applying masking paper, any excess paper should be folded over and secured with tape, or trimmed off. Never leave any loose, unsecured sections of masking paper.

Masking badges, trim and bodywork fittings

Sometimes it may not be possible to remove a particular badge or piece of trim, in which case it will have to be masked **(see illustration 11.8)**.

The best way to go about masking a badge or piece of trim is to stick masking tape over the top of the badge/trim, and around the edges, and then to trim the tape using a very sharp trimming knife. A small plastic or wooden spatula can be used to push the tape into nooks and crannies **(see illustrations 11.9, 11.10 and 11.11)**.

The tape must be cut along the edges of the badge/trim to give a very fine gap between the tape and panel; don't leave the tape touching the panel surface. A very delicate touch will be required to avoid inaccurate cutting and marking the paint surface beneath the tape. It's better to use two or three light passes to cut the tape rather than one heavy pass which cuts into the paint. Make sure that the knife blade is razor-sharp, as otherwise the edge of the

11.9 To mask a badge, stick tape around the edges . . .

11.10 . . . then push the tape into place using a plastic spatula . . .

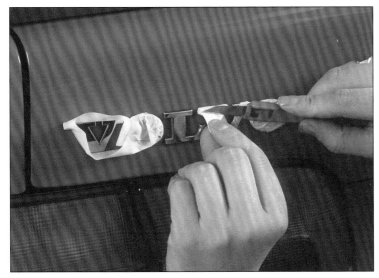

11.11 . . . and trim the edges using a sharp knife

11.12 Fully masked badge

masking tape will tear **(see illustration 11.12)**.

Note that it may be possible to use fine line tape on larger trim pieces or badges.

Masking the gaps between doors and surrounding panels

When spraying panels around doors, or the doors themselves, the masking of the gaps between the doors and surrounding panels is easily overlooked. If these areas are not masked, an accumulation of overspray will build up not only on the sills and door pillars, but also on the inner edges of the doors. This happens because as paint is sprayed through the gaps between the doors, sills and pillars, it bounces off the surfaces to land anywhere it can. This overspray can be very difficult to remove.

When carrying out major spraying work, most professional sprayers prefer to spray the inner edges of a door and door aperture before any other panels are sprayed. Once these areas have cured, the door is closed so that the outer skin and surrounding panels can be sprayed. When the outer door skin is sprayed, the pillar and door aperture must be masked, even if they have already been sprayed.

When spraying a rear door, (or a front door on a two-door or three-door car), a simple method of masking the gap at the rear of the door is to apply a strip of wide masking tape to the edge of the body panel at the rear of the door, with the sticky side facing out. About half the width of the tape is stuck onto the panel, and the rest is folded over at right angles to the panel. A second strip of tape can be applied to the rear edge of the door in the same way, with the sticky side facing out. When the door is shut, the two strips of tape should contact each other and stick together to seal the gap between the door and body **(see illustration 11.13)**.

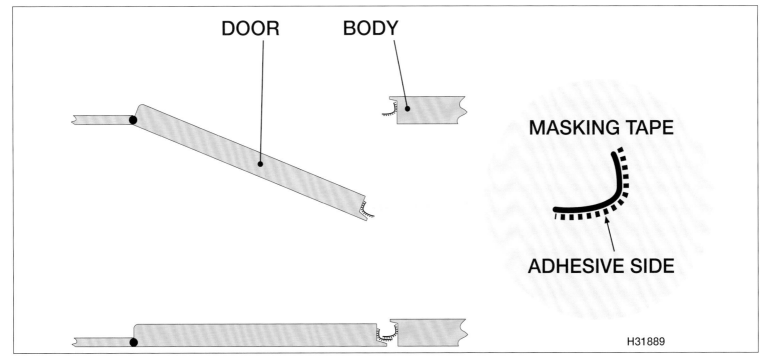

DOOR   BODY

MASKING TAPE

ADHESIVE SIDE

H31889

11.13 Masking the gap between a door and the body using masking tape

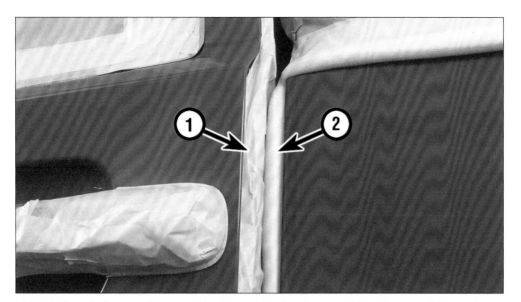

11.14 Gap between door and body masked using masking tape and foam tape

1   *Weatherseal on door masked using tape*
2   *Round-section foam tape applied to body panel*

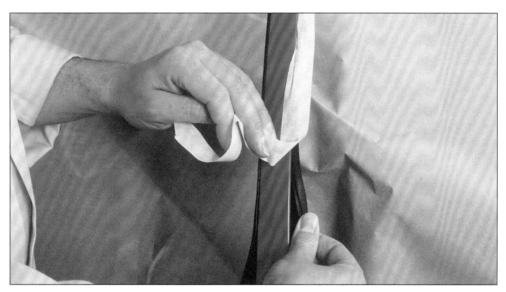

11.15 Masking a door weatherstrip – the tape is slid behind the weatherstrip and wrapped around the rubber

11.16 Using fine line tape to mask along the edge of a window surround

11.17 Door window masking completed ready for spraying door

To mask the gap between front and rear doors, the same method can be used, but the tape is applied to the front edge of the rear door, and the rear edge of the front door. The same technique can also be used for the gaps between the upper and lower door edges and surrounding panels.

Alternatively, round-section foam 'back-masking' tape can be used. In this case, all weatherseals around the edge of the door and/or door aperture should be masked using conventional tape, and foam tape can then be stuck along the rear door pillar. The foam tape should be thick enough to seal the gap between the door and body when the door is closed **(see illustration 11.14)**.

Masking windows

Spraying body panels around windows presents problems with overspray on the weatherstrips and/or trim surrounding the glass. The best way to avoid these problems is to remove the relevant weatherstrips/trim. If this is not possible, fine line tape can be used to mask along the edges of the weatherstrips/trim which adjoin the panel to be sprayed. Masking tape and (where necessary) masking paper can then be taped into place over the remainder of the trim and glass panel, overlapping the fine line tape as described previously **(see illustrations 11.15, 11.16 and 11.17)**.

Masking wheels and wheel arches

If a repair is being sprayed close to a wheel arch, don't forget to mask the wheel, and the inside of the wheel arch.

If this area is overlooked when masking, the resulting overspray can look very unprofessional **(see illustration 11.18)**.

Masking the remaining bodywork

Once all the required masking has been carried out around the area to be sprayed, the remainder of the vehicle must be covered to prevent any possibility of overspray. This is most easily accomplished using a large plastic sheet (usually supplied on rolls by the masking material manufacturers). If necessary, the sheet can be cut to allow for the repair area, and secured using masking tape. Bear in mind the points made earlier regarding keeping the masking material taught, and securing overlapping edges **(see illustration 11.19)**.

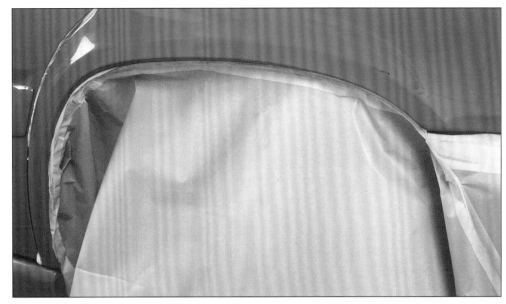

11.18 **Wheel arch and wheel masked using a single sheet of masking paper**

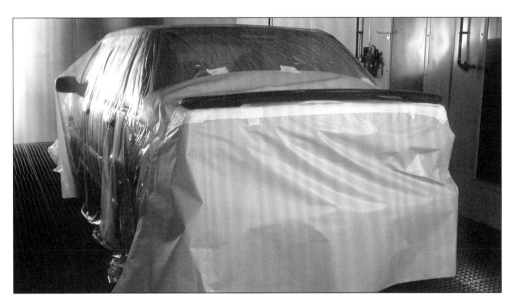

11.19 **Fully masked car (ready for rear spoiler blend repair) positioned in spray booth**

11

Preventing 'hard edges'

As we've already mentioned, a 'hard edge' is one of the worst and most noticeable mistakes which can be made during spraying. A hard edge is produced when paint is sprayed directly up to an edge such as a piece of trim, or masking tape. The build-up of new paint film produces a step between the new paint and the surrounding original finish, and this is highly visible.

To avoid hard edges when spraying up to the edge of a masked badge or a piece of trim, accurate masking is required, as described previously.

When spraying up to the edge of a panel line during a blend repair, or when spraying around door jambs, etc, a technique known as 'back-masking' can be used to avoid hard edges.

Back-masking

If paint is sprayed directly up to a line of masking tape or paper which is stuck to a panel in the conventional manner, it will create a hard edge which can be almost impossible to disguise. This is particularly true if etch primer has been sprayed; because the acid in etch primer eats into the panel and any paint along the masked line, a line will be visible even after the top-coat has been sprayed.

'Back-masking' (also known as 'roll-masking') avoids the creation of hard edges, because it generates slight air turbulence when spraying along the masked edge. As the air and paint swirl around the edge of the tape, the paint will be prevented from finding its way to the edge of the tape, which will produce a feathered effect along the masked edge.

Back-masking is achieved by folding the masking tape back on itself, with the adhesive side facing outwards, to give a rolled edge. The tape can

11.20 To back mask a panel swage line, stick the masking tape along the panel line . . .

11.21 . . . fold the tape over on itself, with the adhesive side facing out . . .

either be stuck to itself, or small additional tabs of tape can be used to secure it in position **(see illustrations 11.20, 11.21 and 11.22)**.

Note that some masking material manufacturers produce a self-adhesive round-section foam tape which can be used to achieve the same effect as back-masking **(see illustration 11.23)**.

Avoiding hard edges around weatherstrips and trim sealing strips

Sometimes it may not be possible to remove certain trim or sealing strips, such as windscreen sealing strips, and trim strips around the edges of windows. In these cases, it's often possible to slide masking tape into the gap between the trim strip and the panel. If the gap is tight, try gently prising the strip away from the edge of the panel using a thin piece of plastic or wood, or a length of plastic cord.

Slide the masking tape under the trim/sealing strip, with its adhesive side facing outwards; ie, with the adhesive side against the trim, not against the body panel. The tape can then be folded over and around the trim/sealing strip in order to mask it.

The fact that the masking tape is stuck around the edge of the trim will help to avoid a hard edge.

Avoiding hard edges at panel joints and swage lines

If a blend repair is being carried out on a panel which is joined to

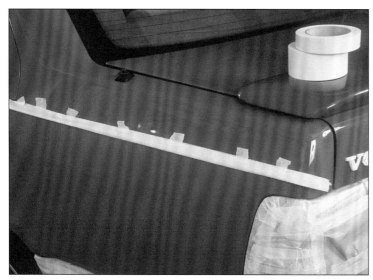

11.22 . . . then secure the tape using tabs

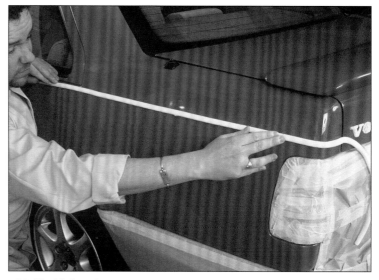

11.23 Using foam tape to mask along a panel swage line

surrounding panels via a welded joint, it's a good idea to mask along the edge of the welded panel join line using the back-masking technique. This will avoid a hard edge, and the welded join line can be used effectively to blend the join between the newly sprayed repair and the original surrounding paint.

This technique can also be used along panel swage lines when carrying out a blend repair **(see illustration 11.24)**.

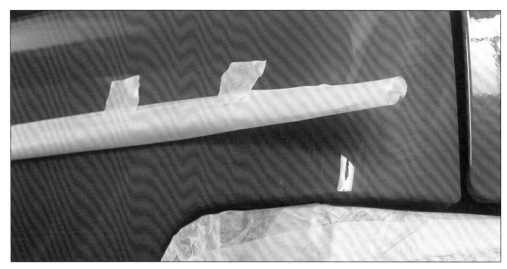

11.24 Back-masking carried out along a panel swage line in preparation for a blend repair

Removing masking materials

Once spraying has been completed, and the paint has cured, the masking materials can be removed.

Although it may be tempting, never rip off masking materials as if you're opening a birthday present! Always pull the tape off gently, at an angle back away from the newly sprayed surface **(see illustration 11.25)**. This will avoid tearing any film of new paint which may have built up to the edge of the tape, and is particularly important when removing tape which has been used to mask up to the edge of a piece of trim, or a badge.

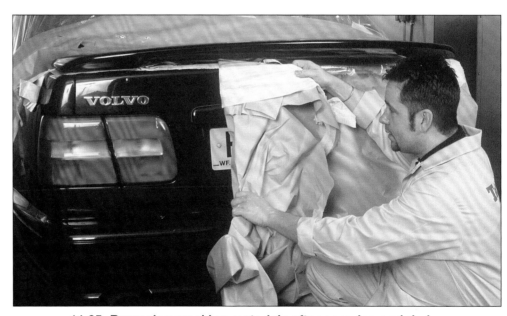

11.25 Removing masking materials after spraying and drying

Notes

Chapter 12
Matching paint colours and mixing paint

Contents

Introduction

Thorough preparation is vital to the final result when carrying out refinishing work, however all the preparation work will be in vain if the final colour coat is not accurately matched to the existing paint on the vehicle. If the colour match is not accurate, the repaired area will be obvious.

Matching and mixing up paint is a vital part of the refinishing process, and it's a skill which can only be learnt by experience. Most people who carry out spraying work regularly build up a mental database of paint colours and the variants used by particular vehicle manufacturers and, in time, accurate colour matching becomes second nature.

Matching paint colours

General

From the explanation of colour composition (see Chapter 2), we can see that the number of colour variations is infinite, which can make paint matching a very difficult process! The final colour produced depends on the quantities of each constituent colour used in the formulation. Even a slight variation in the paint formulation can cause a significant difference in the colour of the final, sprayed paint. Obviously, when manufacturers produce paint, it's very important that they ensure consistency between batches. Although manufacturers are generally very good at keeping paint formulation consistent, sometimes different batches of the same colour vary, and a slightly different colour is produced. Some of the popular colours used by the major vehicle manufacturers may have as many as ten different variations, and it's important to identify exactly which variant has been used before attempting to spray a localised repair.

The major paint manufacturers receive regularly updated information from the vehicle manufacturers about new paint variations, and the paint manufacturers produce a vast range of colour matching charts and samples. These colour matching charts and samples allow a visual check of paint

12.1 Typical paint manufacturer's colour chips

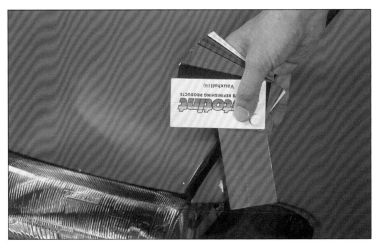

12.2 Using paint manufacturer's colour chips to check the colour against a panel

match to be made against the original paint on the vehicle being sprayed **(see illustrations 12.1 and 12.2)**.

Vehicle paint codes

Most modern vehicles carry a paint code to identify the paint used at the factory when the vehicle was originally sprayed. Often, the paint code is stamped into the Vehicle Identification Number (VIN) plate, but different manufacturers tend to use different locations for the paint code. Some vehicles may even have the paint code located on a label attached to one of the wiring harnesses, or one of the body components, which can make it almost impossible to find. Assuming that the paint code for the vehicle has been found, it may still be necessary to use the vehicle's VIN number or chassis number in conjunction with the paint code to identify the exact colour. Bear in mind that it's possible that the vehicle

may already have been re-sprayed, using an alternative to the original factory colour indicated by the paint code **(see illustrations 12.3 and 12.4)**.

Faded paint

Over a period of time, vehicle paint may fade, which means that localised repairs using paint to the original factory formulation may not be a perfect match for the faded paint on the vehicle. In this case, it may be necessary to mix up a one-off batch of paint to match the faded finish. Some paint manufacturers and suppliers may offer a service where a sample of the paint to be matched can be analysed to enable a matching formulation to be mixed, but this can be time consuming and expensive. Skilled refinishing technicians may be able to mix matching paint formulae themselves (see *Colour variation* in Chapter 2).

Metallic paints

Metallic paint gets its finish from thousands of polished aluminium flakes suspended in the paint. The colour which results depends on the orientation of the flakes, and this in turn depends largely on the spraying conditions when the paint is applied. During spraying, factors which affect the final finish include temperature, humidity, air movement, the quantity of thinners used in the paint, the set-up of the spray gun, the spraying style used, and the drying time. It's particularly important to follow the recommendations given on the paint manufacturer's technical data/application sheet when spraying metallic paint.

When assessing the colour of metallic paint, bear in mind that the angle at which the paint is viewed can make a difference to the appearance of the colour. The aluminium flakes in the

12.3 Typical vehicle manufacturer's paint code location on a Volvo 400 Series

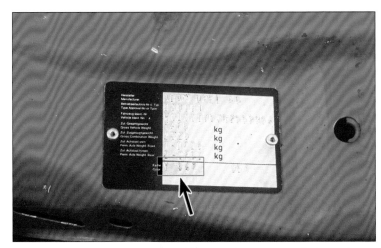

12.4 Typical vehicle manufacturer's paint code location on a Vauxhall Astra

paint act as tiny mirrors which reflect and scatter light according to their orientation in the paint layer. A paint finish where the flakes have settled deep in the paint layer, and are randomly orientated, will look similar regardless of the viewing angle, although a slight difference in tone may be noticed depending on whether the panel is viewed head-on (*face tone*), or from the side (*side tone*). A paint finish where the flakes have settled generally parallel to each other, close to the surface of the paint layer, will appear fairly light when viewed from head-on (a light face tone), but will appear much darker when viewed from an angle (dark side tone) **(see illustrations 12.5 and 12.6)**.

Viewing colours in different lights

The human eye sees colours differently depending on the type of light in which the colour is viewed. Paint viewed under artificial lighting (even ordinary tungsten bulbs) can appear a significantly different colour when compared to how it looks in normal daylight. It's worth taking this effect into account when matching colours, particularly when working under artificial light. Particular problems may be noticed when trying to make a comparison under artificial light between the colour on a panel and the colour on a colour chart or chip. If problems are experienced, it's worth trying another comparison under normal daylight conditions.

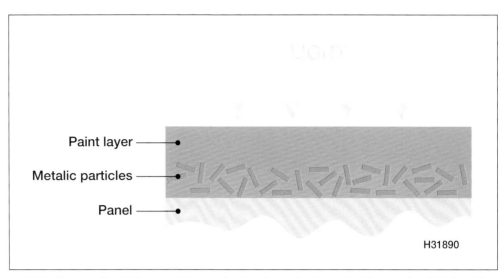

12.5 If metallic flakes settle randomly deep in the paint layer, the finish will look similar regardless of the viewing angle

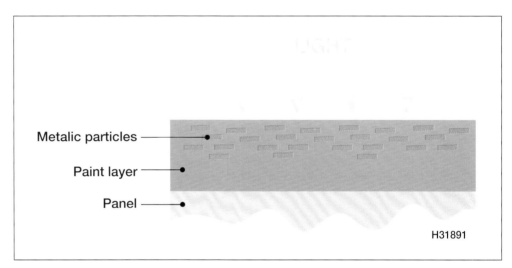

12.6 If metallic flakes settle generally parallel close to the surface of the paint layer, the finish will look lighter or darker depending on the viewing angle

Mixing up paint

Paint colour formulation

Paint manufacturers usually produce lists of paint colour formulations in microfiche form. To find the appropriate colour formulation, first use the paint manufacturer's colour tables and/or chips, in conjunction with the vehicle paint code, to find a match for the paint colour required. When an appropriate colour match is found, note the paint manufacturer's code (and name) for the paint colour required **(see illustrations 12.7 and 12.8)**.

If no paint code can be found on the vehicle, the paint manufacturer's colour chips will have to be used against the existing vehicle paint to find the best colour match.

12.7 Look up the vehicle paint code in the paint manufacturer's colour tables to find the appropriate paint manufacturer's paint reference code . . .

12.8 . . . then check the paint manufacturer's code for a match against the existing vehicle finish using colour chips

12

Typical paint manufacturer's formulation*

Tinter	Volume of paint to be made up			
	0.5 litre	1.0 litre	2.5 litres	4.0 litres
APO118 Perm Red	222.3 g	444.6 g	1111.5 g	1778.4 g
APO160 Red Pearl	333.4 g	666.9 g	1667.2 g	2667.6 g
APO213 Brown	427.9 g	855.8 g	2139.5 g	3423.2 g
APO206 Red Violet	472.3 g	944.7 g	2361.7 g	3778.8 g
APO121 Course Aluminium	478.4 g	956.9 g	2392.2 g	3827.6 g

* Note: *Tetrosyl Autotint formulation for SEAT Rojo Volcan shown*

The paint manufacturer's list of colour formulations can now be consulted. Look up the data for the code (and name) of the paint colour required **(see illustration 12.9)**. An example of typical paint formulation data is shown in the table above; note that all weights are cumulative.

Once the colour to be sprayed has been decided upon, there are three main steps involved in mixing up the paint before it can be sprayed:
1   Mix up the paint colour formulation by weight, according to the paint manufacturer's data.
2   Add the specified quantities of activator (where applicable) and thinner.
3   Check the paint viscosity.

Tinters

The base colours supplied by paint manufacturers, which are mixed together according to a paint formulation to produce a specific colour, are known as *tinters* **(see illustration 12.10)**.

Mixing up a paint colour formulation by weight

Paint is mixed by weight, using very accurate electronic scales. When the total volume of paint required has been decided (eg, 1 litre), the paint manufacturer's formulation can be checked to determine the various weights of tinter which need to be mixed to form the desired colour. Always plan to make up a little more paint than is actually required.

Before attempting to mix up paint, switch on the tinter agitator (a power agitator is usually built into the tinter storage rack), and agitate the tinters for the recommended time (see *Paint mixing equipment* in Chapter 6).
1   Begin by placing the container in which the paint is to be mixed on the

12.9 Looking up a paint manufacturer's colour formulation on microfiche

12.10 A rack of typical tinters in a paint shop

12.11 Place the paint container on the scales, then zero the scales

12.12 Pour the first tinter into the container until the required weight is reached

scales, then zero the scales **(see illustration 12.11)**.

2   Slowly pour the first tinter into the container on the scales until the required weight is reached **(see illustration 12.12)**.

3   Repeat the process with the remaining tinter(s) until the final specified weight is reached **(see illustration 12.13)**. Note that the weights specified are normally cumulative, so there's no need to carry out calculations; simply add the relevant tinter until the next recommended weight is reached (see *Paint colour formulation* for a typical example of a colour formulation).

4   Once all the relevant tinters have been added, stir the mixture thoroughly by hand using a suitable stirrer **(see illustration 12.14)**.

5   Carry out a visual colour check. Ideally, the colour should be checked against the existing colour on the vehicle panel, but if this isn't possible, the colour can be checked against the paint manufacturer's colour charts or

chips **(see illustration 12.15)**. Provided that the paint colour is satisfactory, the paint is now ready for the addition of thinner (where necessary) and any other additives required (such as activator when working with 2-pack paints).

Adding activator and thinner

In most cases, concentrated paint will have to be thinned before it can be sprayed. Additionally, when working with 2-pack paints, precise quantities of activator (hardener) must be added. Once the appropriate tinters have been mixed to give the desired colour of paint, activator (where applicable) and thinner must be added before the paint can be used. Thinner and activator recommendations will be provided on the relevant paint technical data/application sheet.

It's important to note that the temperature at which a paint is sprayed and dried can have a significant effect on the finish, because the viscosity of the paint will vary with temperature. For

this reason, when using certain types of paint, different types of thinners are available for use in different ambient temperatures. The paint technical data/application sheet should give recommendations for the type of thinner to be used for a particular spraying temperature. Many professional sprayers tailor the exact amount of thinner to their personal preferences, based on the paint manufacturer's recommendations.

When working with 2-pack paints, note that once activator has been added, there is a limited amount of time before the paint begins to cure. For this reason, activator and thinner should not be added until shortly before the paint is to be sprayed. Before adding activator and thinner, make sure that the spray gun has been cleaned, and is ready for spraying. Check that the spray gun is set up correctly for the particular paint to be sprayed (see Chapter 8).

As well as the recommended paint-to-thinner mixing ratio, the paint technical data/application sheet will

12

12.13 Repeat the process with the remaining tinters . . .

12.14 . . . then stir the mixture thoroughly

12.15 Checking the colour against the paint manufacturer's colour chips

12.16 Pour the mixed colour into a clean container with appropriate mixing rule

12.17 Continue pouring until the level reaches the appropriate level mark on the mixing rule

12.18 Add the required quantity of activator . . .

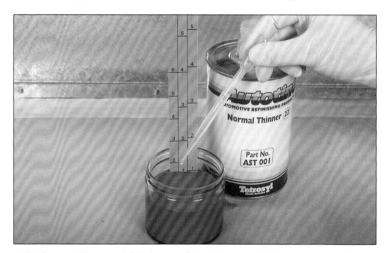

12.19 . . . then add thinner (pipette used for accuracy) . . .

normally give details of the recommended viscosity of the paint for spraying. The viscosity can be checked before spraying as described later in this Chapter.

Once the colour has been mixed, activator (where applicable) and thinner should be added as follows.

1 Pour the mixed colour from the vessel used for mixing into a suitable measuring cup with a scale, or alternatively into a clean container with an appropriate mixing rule (suitable measuring cups and/or mixing rules are available from paint manufacturers). Pour in the colour until the level reaches the appropriate level mark on the measuring cup or mixing rule **(see illustrations 12.16 and 12.17)**.

2 Where applicable, when mixing up 2-pack paints, add activator (hardener) until the fluid level reaches the appropriate level mark on the measuring cup or mixing rule **(see illustration 12.18)**. To improve accuracy as the level mark is approached, a clean pipette can be used to add drops of activator. Take care not to add too much activator.

3 Add thinner until the fluid level reaches appropriate level mark on the measuring cup or mixing rule. Again, to improve accuracy as the level mark is approached, a clean pipette can be used to add drops of thinner **(see illustrations 12.19 and 12.20)**. Take care not to add too much thinner.

4 Once the appropriate quantities of colour, activator (where applicable) and thinner have been added, stir the mixture thoroughly by hand **(see illustration 12.21)**. The viscosity of the paint can now be checked against the paint manufacturer's recommendations as follows.

12.20 . . . until the appropriate level on the mixing rule is reached . . .

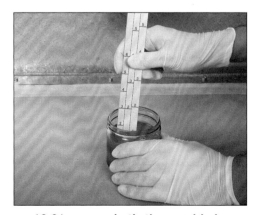

12.21 . . . and stir thoroughly by hand

Checking paint viscosity

Once paint has been mixed up ready for spraying (see *Mixing up paint*), the viscosity of the paint should be checked to make sure that it meets the manufacturer's recommendations, as follows. A suitable viscosity measuring vessel and a stop watch will be required for this check. Before carrying out viscosity measurements, make sure that the ambient temperature is within the limits specified by the paint manufacturer.

1   Select a suitable standard paint viscosity measuring vessel, in accordance with the paint manufacturer's recommendations **(see illustration 12.22)**.

2   Hold a finger over the hole in the end of the vessel, then pour in paint until the level reaches the appropriate level mark on the vessel **(see illustration 12.23)**.

3   Position the measuring vessel over a container to catch the escaping paint, then release the finger from the hole in the end of the vessel, at the same time starting the stop watch **(see illustration 12.24)**. Measure the time taken for all the paint to run from the vessel, and stop the stop watch when the last drop drips from the hole (the paint flow will usually stop cleanly and quickly).

4   Check the time taken for the vessel

to empty against the time specified by the paint manufacturer.

5   If necessary, add additional thinner, and repeat the test until the paint meets the recommended viscosity.

Once the colour match and viscosity are satisfactory, the paint can be poured into the spray gun paint reservoir, ready for spraying. Always use a filter when pouring the paint into the spray gun reservoir to prevent any contamination from entering the reservoir **(see illustration 12.25)**.

With the spray gun set up for spraying (see Chapter 8), a final colour check can be made by test-spraying a spray-out card (see Chapter 13).

12.22 **Select a suitable viscosity measuring vessel . . .**

12.23 **. . . then hold finger over the hole, and pour in paint until the level reaches the level mark**

12.24 **Release the finger, and measure the time taken for all the paint to run from the vessel**

12.25 **Pour the paint into the spray gun paint reservoir using a filter**

12

Notes

Chapter 13
Spraying technique

Contents

Introduction

Spraying technique is something which can only be learnt through practical experience, and becoming a skilled sprayer will take time **(see illustration 13.1)**.

Although there are basic rules to follow, the finer points of how a spraying job is approached are very much influenced by how the sprayer has been trained, and by personal preference; one sprayer may approach a particular job in a slightly different way from a colleague who prefers an alternative technique, but both sprayers will probably achieve the same end result.

This Chapter is not intended to form a set of rules, but aims to provide advice on how to avoid some of the common pitfalls when spraying, and how to achieve a professional finish.

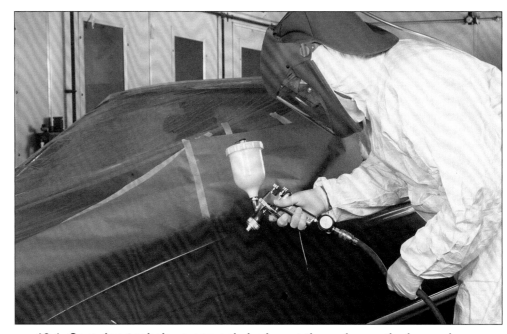

13.1 Spraying technique can only be learnt through practical experience

13

Preparation

Good preparation is absolutely vital for a professional finish. Even the most skilled sprayer will not be able to hide the effects of poor preparation.

The aim must be to provide a spotlessly clean, smooth surface to which paint can be applied. Any surface blemishes, contaminants, or dirt will show through the paint layers, and will be visible in the final finish, providing an obvious indication that refinishing work has been carried out.

All the work carried out prior to spraying must be carried out thoroughly – don't be tempted to cut corners in order to save time. For example if body filler is used, allow adequate time for the filler to harden properly before sanding, and don't be tempted to use additional activator to reduce the curing time (see Chapter 10). Although time is money in a body shop environment, cutting corners will lead to time wasting and increased costs in the long run (as well as possibly a reputation for poor workmanship) **(see illustration 13.2)**.

13.2 Good preparation is vital

Each individual step in the refinishing process is of equal importance to the end result. It's all too easy to consider preparation work as a necessary chore which must be carried out before spraying.

Cleanliness

Cleanliness throughout the refinishing process is essential. Dust and dirt at the sprayer's worst enemies, and great care must be taken to avoid contamination at each stage of the refinishing process. Also bear in mind that any greases and oils are likely to cause blemishes in the final finish.

The following precautions will help to avoid contamination during the preparation process.

• Avoid using space heaters in a body shop environment (they disturb dust, and create fumes which can cause contamination).

• Keep doors and window closed (to reduce dust).

• Always wear non-absorbent (latex) gloves. This will prevent oils and greases from the skin from causing contamination. Gloves are also essential to protect the skin from the chemicals used during refinishing work.

• Use dust extraction wherever possible when carrying out sanding operations.

• Use panel wipe to clean the repair area before and after each stage in the process.

• Use a tack cloth to remove any small dirt and dust particles immediately before spraying **(see illustration 13.3)**.

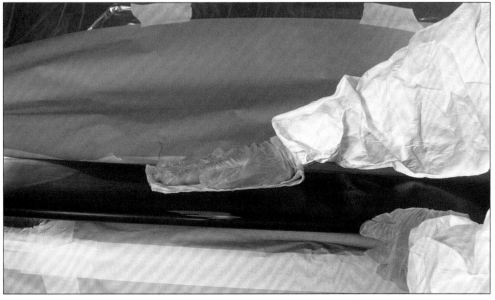

13.3 Use a tack cloth to remove any dirt and dust immediately before spraying

Setting up a spray gun

Before spraying, the spray gun should be set up to suit the paint being used, and the spray pattern should be checked. Refer to Chapter 8 for details.

Manoeuvring a spray gun

General

The ideal way to manoeuvre a spray gun during spraying will depend on the size and location of the area being sprayed.

There are three elements of the spraying action which will have a direct effect on the results produced:

• The orientation of the spray gun in relation to the panel being sprayed **(see illustration 13.4)**.

• The speed of spray gun movement **(see illustration 13.5)**.

• The distance from the gun nozzle to the panel being sprayed **(see illustration 13.6)**.

To produce good results when spraying, it's important to be relaxed and comfortable. It's easy to feel awkward when first using a spray gun, and it will take practise before a natural spraying action is developed.

The best stance for spraying is with the legs slightly apart, so that weight is evenly distributed between the legs. It's important for a sprayer to allow their body to move with the gun; this will produce a much smoother action than if the body is held still with all movement starting at the shoulder.

Most spray guns give the best results when they are held at right-angles to the surface to be sprayed, at a distance of around 150 to 200 mm, or approximately one hand-span away (with fingers and thumb outstretched).

Spray gun trigger action

When partial pressure is applied to a spray gun trigger, the air valve opens to allow air to pass through the gun at spraying pressure (no paint will be sprayed at this stage) **(see**

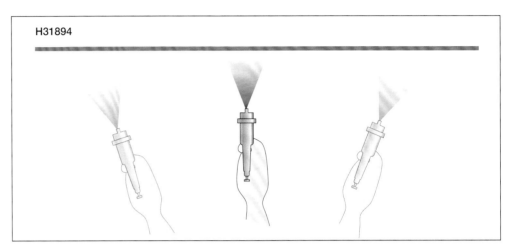

13.4 The results produced by a spray gun are affected by the orientation of the spray gun . . .

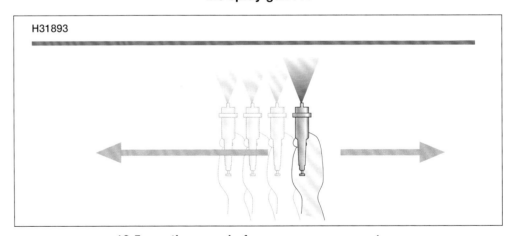

13.5 . . . the speed of spray gun movement . . .

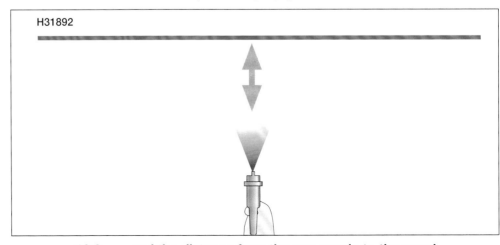

13.6 . . . and the distance from the gun nozzle to the panel

13

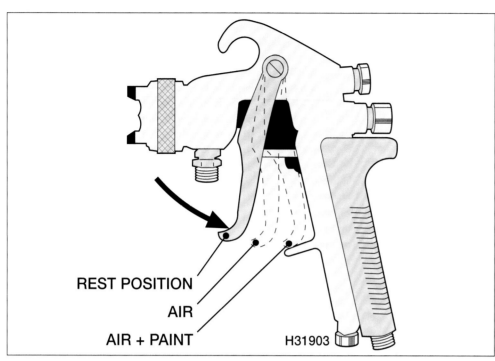

13.7 Partial pressure on the spray gun trigger will allow air to pass through the gun, and full pressure will spray paint

illustration **13.7)**. When the trigger is pulled fully, the fluid needle will move, and paint will be sprayed.

Starting and finishing a spray pass

A spray pass should always be started off the area to be sprayed.
1 Start the gun moving towards the edge of the repair area with the trigger partially depressed, so that just air is flowing through the gun.
2 As the gun nears the edge of the repair area, squeeze the trigger further to introduce paint to the spray.
3 Keep the trigger fully depressed as the gun is moved across the repair area until just after the remaining edge of the area is crossed.
4 Once the gun is clear of the edge of the repair area, release the pressure on the trigger back to the 'air on' position to stop the paint flow – do not fully release the trigger.
5 Move the gun into position ready for the next pass, and repeat the procedure.

Never attempt to start the paint flow at the moment the gun reaches the edge of the repair area, as this will usually result in the formation of a 'dry edge', giving a poor finish. Always make sure that paint is flowing before moving the gun across the repair area.

Spraying complete panels and large areas

When spraying anything other than a spot repair, the aim is to keep the spray gun moving parallel to the panel at all times **(see illustration 13.8)**. If the gun is kept parallel and at right-angles to the panel, the spray pattern will be uniform. If the gun is swung in an arc, the distance from the gun nozzle to the panel will vary, and more paint will hit the surface in the areas where the nozzle is closer. This will not only produce an uneven coating, but will also result in paint in the middle of the arc drying more slowly than the paint at the ends of the arc, which can give variations in colour, and can cause blemishes.

The gun should be kept at right-angles to the panel at all times, both vertically and horizontally, and this will mean following any curves in the panel **(see illustration 13.9)**. The wrist and

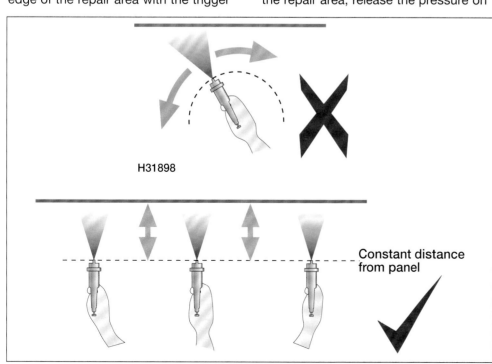

13.8 The spray gun should be moved parallel to the panel at all times. Do not swing the spray gun in an arc

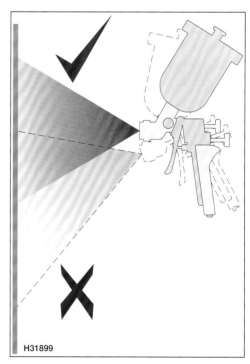

13.9 The spray gun should be kept at right-angles to the panel at all times, both vertically and horizontally

elbow should be locked when moving the gun, and when spraying a large area, or a complete vehicle, the arm and shoulder should also be locked, moving from one panel to another in a smooth, steady walk.

The edge of each spray pass should overlap the previous pass by approximately half **(see illustration 13.10)**. When spraying directly up to the edge of a masked area, the centre of the first pass should be aimed directly along the edge of the masking, with half the spray on the masked area, and half the spray on the panel.

Spraying a spot repair

If a small spot repair is being sprayed, it may actually be desirable to move the spray gun in an arc (using a wrist action), in order to feather the paint at the edges of the sprayed area. This technique takes some practise!

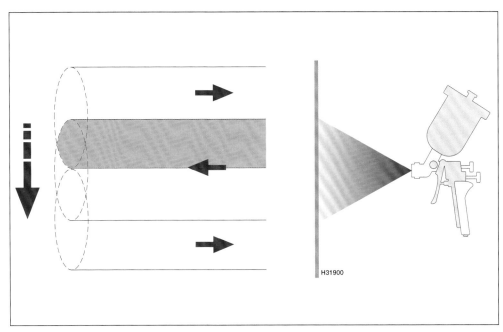

13.10 The edge of each spray pass should overlap the previous pass by approximately half

Replicating the manufacturer's finish

Once the basic skills of spraying have been mastered, it's important to realise that when spraying a repair, the aim of the skilled sprayer is to replicate the vehicle manufacturer's paint finish, so that the repaired area is undetectable.

At this point, it's worth pointing out that few vehicle manufacturer's produce vehicles with a perfect finish! It's often the case that if a perfect finish is achieved when spraying the repair, the repair will stand out because the surrounding original paintwork is not perfect.

Replicating the manufacturer's finish is a skill which can only be developed with experience. An experienced sprayer will know which manufacturer's vehicles have a near perfect finish, and which vehicles have a finish with a degree of 'orange peel'.

With experience, a skilled sprayer will be able to set up the spray gun to give a similar quality of finish (for example, the same degree of 'orange peel') to the original finish surrounding the repair.

Spray-out card check

When spraying colour coat, once the spray gun reservoir has been filled with paint, and the spray gun has been set up for spraying, a final check should be made on the colour match. This is done using a spray-out card.

Different types of spray-out card are available, but a typical example consists of a card with black and white stripes **(see illustration 13.11)**.

With the example shown, the card should be secured to a suitable surface, and then sprayed until none of the black or white areas are visible, and an even colour is produced. This should give a sufficient thickness of paint to provide an accurate sample for colour matching against the existing paint on the vehicle **(see illustration 13.12)**.

Allow the paint on the spray-out card to dry thoroughly, then check the colour against that on the vehicle.

13

13.11 Typical spray-out card

13.12 Spray the card until an even colour is produced

Spraying a blend repair

A 'blend repair' is considered to be a spot repair on a panel which requires blending in with the surrounding paintwork.

Assessing the repair

When carrying out a blend repair, it's necessary to assess the area around the repair to decide how best to carry out blending. The object of the blending exercise is to hide the repair, blending it in with the surrounding paintwork so that it's undetectable. There are several factors to consider when deciding on the extent of blending required **(see illustration 13.13)**.

• If the finish has a clear lacquer coat, assess the area of existing lacquer which will have to be flatted to enable blending with the new lacquer sprayed over the repair.

• Consider the angle of the panel, and decide whether this affects the extent of the blending required (this

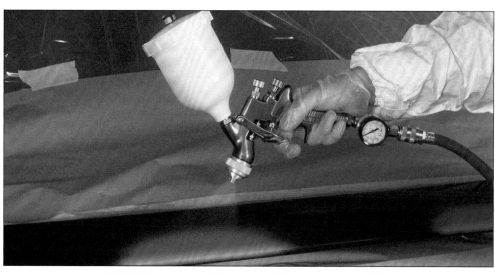

13.13 Spraying a blend repair on a rear spoiler

applies particularly to metallic and pearlescent finishes).

• Consider whether there are any swage lines or panel edges which can be used to help in blending the repair.

• Decide on the extent of masking required, and whether it will be

necessary to remove any trim or door fittings, etc.

Repair procedure

Refer to Chapter 17 for an example of a typical blend repair carried out when repairing a scratched panel.

Spraying a new panel

When spraying a new panel, it may still be necessary to blend in the finish with surrounding panels to prevent the repair being obvious.

Assessing the repair

As with any repair, when spraying a new panel, the aim is to ensure that the paint on the new panel blends in with the surrounding paintwork, so that the repair is undetectable.

There are several factors to consider when deciding on deciding on how best to spray a new panel **(see illustration 13.14)**.

• Decide on whether there are any areas of the new panel which require treatment with products such as underseal, stone-chip protection, sound-deadening material, etc.

• If the finish has a clear lacquer coat,

assess the area of existing lacquer on the panels surrounding the new panel which will have to be flatted to enable blending with the new panel (for example, if a new front wing panel is being fitted, it is common practise to flat and lacquer the front door to aid blending of the repair).

• Consider the angle of the panel, and the surrounding panels, and decide whether this is likely to affect the extent of any blending required (this applies particularly to metallic and pearlescent finishes).

• Decide on the extent of masking required, and whether it will be necessary to remove any trim or door fittings, light units, etc.

• Consider whether it is necessary to spray any inaccessible areas of the panel before the panel is fitted (eg, the edges of the panel which will not be within the area of the spray pattern once the panel is fitted).

Repair procedure

Refer to Chapter 17 for an example of a typical procedure for spraying a new panel.

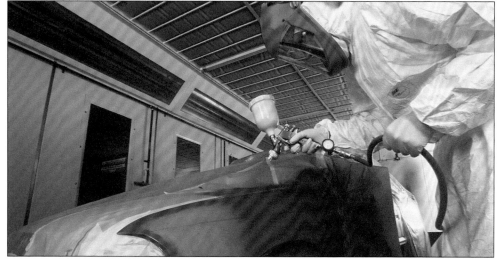

13.14 Spraying a new front wing panel

Spraying a complete vehicle

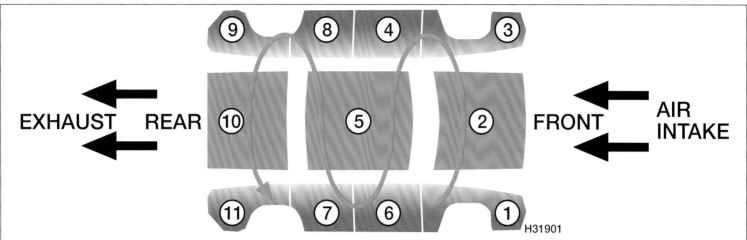

13.15 Typical spraying pattern when spraying a complete vehicle in a cross-draught spray booth

When spraying a complete vehicle, it's important to have a clear plan of action in place before commencing spraying.

Ensure that all relevant components such as light units, door handles, etc, have been removed, and relevant areas such as windows, weatherstrips, light apertures, wheels, etc, are masked.

The order in which panels are sprayed is important, and experienced sprayers tend to have their own personal preferences. Here are a few points to bear in mind.

• Bear in mind that by the time spraying starts on the final panel, the paint on the first panel sprayed will have begun to cure.

• Obviously, individual panels cannot be masked, and so the spraying must be planned so that the overspray from one panel does not land on another panel on which the paint has begun to cure.

• The order of panel spraying will be affected to an extent by the type of

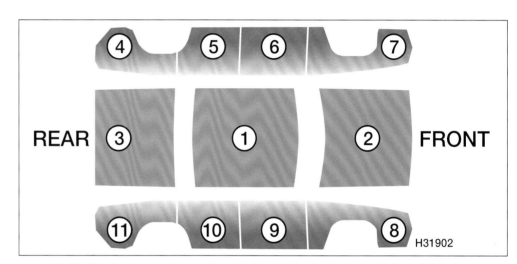

13.16 Typical spraying pattern when spraying a complete vehicle in a downdraught spray booth

spray booth used. For example, a cross-draught spray booth will tend to pull overspray towards one end of the vehicle, whereas a down-draught spray booth will tend to pull overspray down (cross-draught booths are rare in the UK due to EPA legislation). Suggestions for spraying sequences for use with a cross-draught spray booth and a down-draught spray booth are given in the accompanying illustrations **(see illustrations 13.15 and 13.16)**.

Spraying etch primer

13

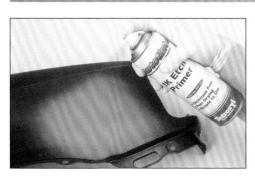

13.17 Spraying a local repair with etch primer from an aerosol

Etch primers should be sprayed onto bare metal or filler. Etch primers are designed to provide anti-corrosion protection (see *Paints* in Chapter 7).

Most etch primers require the addition of an activated thinner before spraying. Some manufacturers produce etch primers in aerosol form for use when touching up localised chipping or

carrying out spot repairs **(see illustration 13.17)**.

Generally, etch primers don't require sanding, and high-build primer is usually sprayed over the top before preparing the panel to receive colour coat. This is known as a 'wet-on-wet' or 'non-sand' process.

Note that some etch primers are not suitable for use on certain plastics.

Spraying high-build primer

High-build primers are designed to fill any small imperfections in a panel, and to provide a smooth finish and a good key for the spraying of colour coat.

Thinner and activator (where applicable) should be added to high-build primer in accordance with the paint manufacturer's recommendations. The manufacturer's technical data/application sheet will normally give recommendations on sanding and flatting.

The spraying of high-build primer is the last spraying stage before spraying top-coat, and so care should be taken to produce a high-quality finish during spraying.

Spraying colour coat and lacquer

Colour coats should be mixed and sprayed in accordance with the paint manufacturer's technical data/ application sheet, and particular care must be taken to spray smooth, even coats.

If a colour base coat is being sprayed which requires a clear lacquer coat to be sprayed over the top, the lacquer coat is usually sprayed before the colour coat has fully cured. Refer to the paint technical data/application sheet for details of the maximum time allowed between application of the base and lacquer coats.

Chapter 14
Paint drying

Contents

Introduction

When a vehicle is originally painted at the factory, the paint is sprayed onto the bare body panels before the trim and accessory items, door handles, etc, are fitted. The paint can then be dried by high-temperature baking (200°C or more) in a drying oven. Even if it was suitable for the paint products being used, this high-temperature baking cannot be used when carrying out refinishing work, because damage would be caused to plastic and rubber parts, as well as sensitive electronic components.

There are three basic methods of drying paint when refinishing; air drying, drying in a low-bake oven, or drying under infra-red lamps. Note that most automotive paints do not specifically

require heat to dry, but heat speeds up the drying process, which is all-important in a commercial environment.

Air drying, which involves simply leaving the paint to dry naturally, with no artificial heating, is rarely used in a professional refinishing environment. Virtually all professional body shops are equipped with a low-bake oven, often combined with a spray booth. Many body shops also have infra-red drying lamps, which are available in portable form, or may be built into a spray booth.

When using most professional solvent and water-based paints, there are two distinct stages to the drying process. First of all there is a 'flash-off' period, during which the solvents in the paint evaporate. Once the solvents

have evaporated, the curing process begins. A 2-pack paint will begin to cure due to a chemical reaction once activator is added, but heat is used to speed up the chemical reaction.

Note that although paint may appear dry after using a low-bake oven or infra-red lamps, in some cases it may take several days or even weeks for the paint to fully harden. Check the paint manufacturer's recommendations for details of the recommended curing time to be allowed before compounding and polishing of fresh paint can be carried out.

Specific drying recommendations for paint will be found on the paint manufacturer's technical data/application sheet.

14

Flash-off times

The 'flash-off time' is the recommended time for which a coat of paint must be left to air dry after spraying, to allow most of the volatile solvent material in the paint to evaporate. Flash-off times will normally be given in the paint manufacturer's technical data/application sheet.

Once a coat of paint has been sprayed, care must be taken to allow the recommended flash-off time before spraying another coat. If another coat of paint is sprayed too soon, before most of the solvent has evaporated from the first coat, it can lead to blemishes and blisters in the final finish, as the solvent tries to evaporate through the paint layers **(see illustration 14.1)**.

When drying paint, the recommended flash-off time must be observed before applying heat. If too

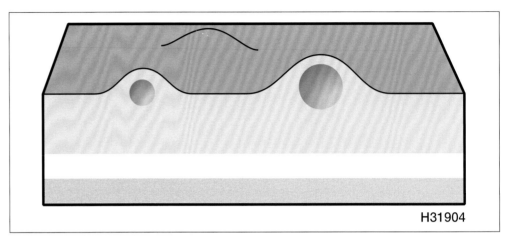

14.1 If the recommended flash-off time is not observed, solvent bubbles can cause blemishes in the finish

much heat is applied before the recommended flash time has elapsed, too much solvent can evaporate too quickly, and the surface of the paint

may dry. A dry skin on the paint surface will prevent solvent bubbles from escaping, producing blemishes in the finish.

Air drying

Air drying involves simply leaving the paint to dry naturally, in a dust-free environment, with no artificial heating. Air drying may be used on primer coats (eg, etch primer) which can be re-coated or sprayed over in a relatively short time (ie, wet-on-wet application) before they have fully cured. Air drying of large painted areas and top-coats is not practical in a body shop environment; it take hours as opposed to minutes, and the vehicle or panel(s) must be left in a dust and dirt-free environment throughout the drying process.

Drying using a low-bake oven

All professional bodyshops use a low-bake oven for drying paint. In many cases, a combined spray booth/low-bake oven will be used, but alternatively, a body shop with a high throughput of vehicles may have separate spray booths and low-bake ovens. A low-bake oven provides a clean environment for paint drying, with precise control of the temperature and air flow.

Spray booths and low-bake ovens are the most expensive items of equipment used in a body shop, and

the exact type and specification of equipment used will depend on the budget available, the amount of work carried out, and the layout of the body shop.

Most low-bake ovens operate at a temperature of around 60 to 80°C, to give a metal panel temperature of around 60°C. This temperature will accelerate the chemical reaction which dries the paint, and will also accelerate the evaporation of any solvents remaining in the paint after the flash-off period.

Raising the temperature

If the drying temperature is raised too fast, bubbles and blemishes may form in the paint finish, and the surface of the paint surface will dry before the underlying layers, forming a 'skin'. Any remaining solvent in the paint cannot evaporate through the paint skin into the atmosphere, and so bubbles of solvent will form near the surface of the paint. This problem can be avoided by observing the recommended flash-off time before applying heat, and by raising the temperature in the low-bake oven in controlled stages.

Airflow

All types of paint, particularly water-based paints, benefit from a high airflow during flash-off and during the early stages of curing, and air movement is just as important as the temperature used to dry the paint **(see illustration 14.2)**. Drying technology is progressing constantly, and most modern ovens incorporate advanced high airflow technology. It's also possible to obtain additional stand-alone airflow enhancement (blower) equipment, which can be placed inside an oven to assist the drying process. The draw-back of stand-alone systems is the increased risk of contamination from dirt and dust.

During the drying process, air is normally recirculated, which saves on heating energy. As a safety measure, a fresh-air bleed system introduces a measured quantity of fresh air to absorb vapours released during the drying process, and fuel vapour from vehicle fuel tanks, etc.

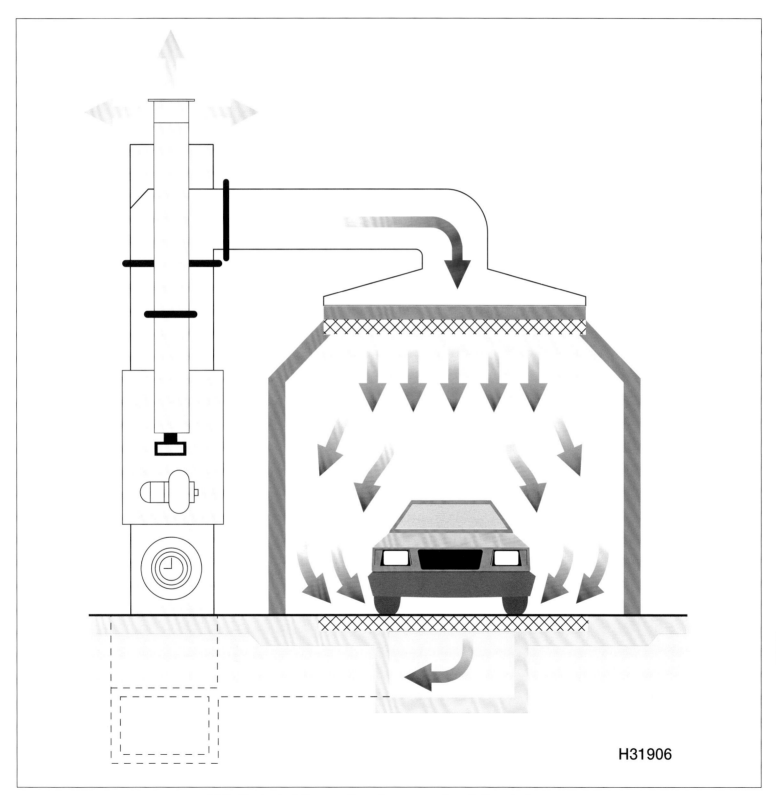

H31906

14.2 Typical airflow pattern in a spray booth/low-bake oven

Controls

Oven controls will vary depending on the type of equipment used **(see illustration 14.3)**. Some basic units may have fully manual controls (temperature and drying time), while most modern units will have fully automatic drying programmes which can be selected using electronic controls (many of these systems incorporate a fault diagnosis system to provide warning and identification of any faults with the equipment). Once a drying cycle is selected, the oven will normally increase the temperature in set stages, and carry out a purging process to purge solvent vapours before switching off.

If a manually-controlled oven is being used, it's particularly important to understand and follow the recommended operating procedure. For example, if a combined spray booth/oven is being used, the booth must be purged of vapours before the drying process begins, and when drying, the temperature must be raised in controlled stages.

Further details of how a low-bake oven operates can be found in Chapter 6.

Safety considerations

In terms of danger to health, the forced drying procedure using a low-bake oven is probably the most dangerous stage of the refinishing process. Not only is a high temperature used, but the oven will be full of solvent vapours as they evaporate from the paint.

Ovens are fitted with various safety systems to ensure that the vapours are contained (and filtered before they are released into the atmosphere), and that no-one can remain inside, or enter the oven, when it's operating.

The biggest danger when using a low-bake oven is fire. Paints, solvents, petrol in vehicle fuel tanks, masking

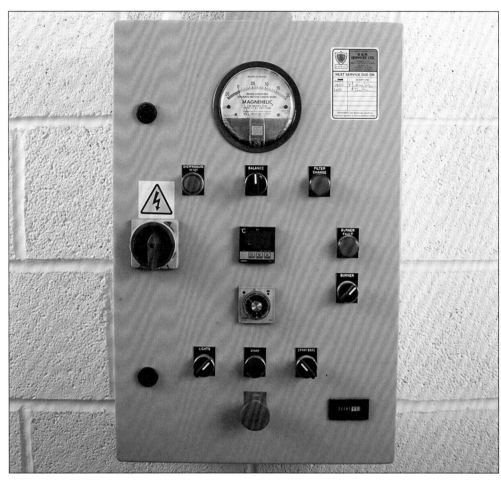

14.3 Typical spray booth/low-bake oven control

materials, and vehicle components are all potential fire hazards. All electrical equipment associated with the spray booth/oven must be installed outside the main booth enclosure, where possible. When a vehicle is being dried in a low-bake oven, the most likely circumstances for an fire or explosion are when a fuel leak develops before or during the paint drying process. Normal vapour leakage from the fuel filler cap should not be a problem, and will be absorbed by the oven's fresh air bleed system, but leaks of liquid petrol can cause a serious problem. Before a vehicle is placed in an oven, certain precautions can be taken to guard

against fuel leakage problems. Any open fuel lines (open lines due to component or engine removal for instance) should be sealed, and the fuel filler cap should be slackened to prevent a build-up of pressure.

Vehicles should not be baked for longer than necessary, and the booth electrical equipment should be checked regularly. Refer to Chapter 3 for general safety recommendations.

Using a low-bake oven

Low-bake ovens should be operated in accordance with the manufacturer's manual, and the relevant paint manufacturer's recommendations.

Infra-red drying

The advantage of infra-red drying equipment is that it's available in portable form, and can be positioned to dry a spot repair of individual panels, without the need to heat the entire vehicle. Portable infra-red equipment is generally used outside the spay booth/low-bake oven, in a clean, ventilated preparation area **(see illustration 14.4)**.

In recent years, there has been a significant increase in the use of infra-red drying systems in spray booths, and the trend is towards systems specifically designed to fit in a spray booth, running on tracks or rails. Some systems are even designed to move automatically over selected areas of a vehicle to assist drying. If infra-red equipment is used in a spray booth, there are two problems; overspray and safety. Sources of heat, or ignition, are dangerous in an environment where paint spray is present, and safety systems must be in place to ensure that spraying cannot be carried out whilst infra-red lamps are switched on. Generally speaking, only purpose-built units should be used in spray booths.

Using infra-red lamps

The first thing to bear in mind when using infra-red lamps is safety. Lamps get hot! Although the radiation produced by a short-wave lamp is visible, the heat is intense. When using medium-wave lamps, bear in mind that although there may be no visible sign that the unit is switched on (other than a warning light), heat is still produced, and the ceramic plates take some time to cool once the lamp has been switched off.

Most units have automatic timers; the lamp is positioned at the specified distance from the panel, and the required drying time is then set on the control unit. Once the lamp has been activated, it will switch off automatically after the set time.

When using infra-red lamps, always observe the manufacturers operating instructions, particularly the recommended distance between the lamp head and the panel to be dried. Refer to the paint manufacturer's technical data/application sheet for recommended drying times.

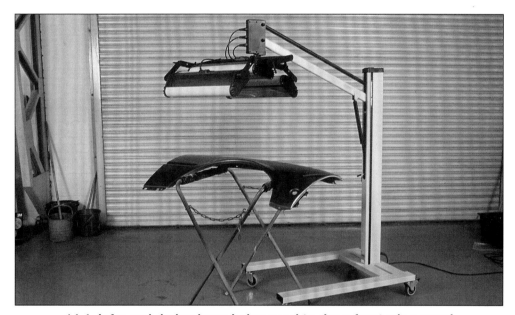

14.4 Infra-red drying lamp being used to dry a front wing panel

14

Notes

Chapter 15
Sanding, de-nibbing and flatting

Contents

Introduction

Sanding and flatting are essential steps in the refinishing process. The sanding and flatting processes are just as critical as the paint spraying operation, as any blemishes or flaws in the prepared surface will be magnified by the application of paint.

Sanding operations can be divided into two broad categories;

• Sanding to remove corrosion, etc, before applying body filler.
• Sanding to provide a smooth surface in preparation for the application of paint (primer or top-coat) **(see illustration 15.1)**.

De-nibbing is essentially a very light local sanding process, used to remove 'nibs' in newly-sprayed paintwork. Nibs may be due to minor contamination from dust and dirt particles, or from small insects, during paint drying.

Flatting can be considered to be a very light sanding operation, used to remove the gloss from an existing painted or lacquered surface to provide a key for new paint to adhere.

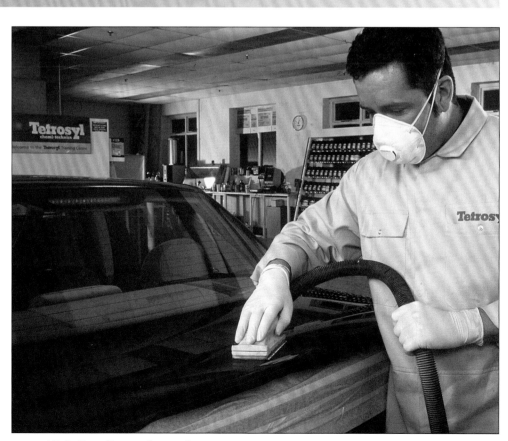

15.1 Sanding paintwork to remove a scratch, before applying primer

15

Sanding

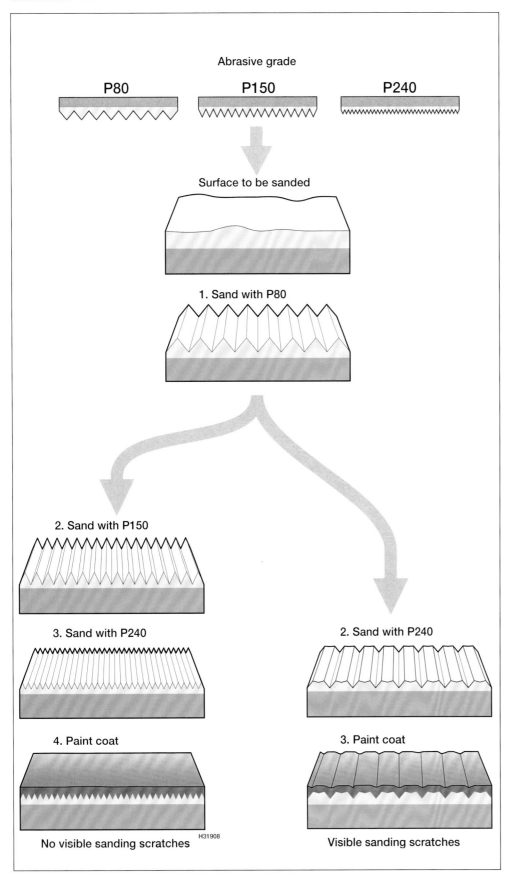

15.2 Always use progressively finer grades of abrasive paper (shown at left). A large jump from coarse to fine (shown at right) will leave sanding scratches in the finish.

Regardless of the type of surface which is to be painted, whether it be body filler or an existing paint finish, some sanding will be required. Sanding can be done by hand, or using a power sander – refer to Chapter 6 for details of the equipment available.

There are a few basic rule to observe when carrying out any sanding operation;

• Use dust extraction equipment wherever possible.
• When sanding by hand, always use a sanding block.
• Wherever possible sanding should be carried out dry. Some abrasives are designed to be used with water to prevent clogging and to act as a lubricant, but water can sometimes be absorbed into the substrate or existing paint layers, and can cause problems with the final finish.
• Never use water when sanding body filler. Body filler absorbs water readily, which will lead to corrosion of metal substrates, and blemishes in the final finish.
• Sand using progressively finer grades of abrasive paper, depending on the work being carried out. If a large jump is made from a coarse abrasive to a very fine abrasive, the fine abrasive will not cover the sanding marks left by the coarse abrasive **(see illustration 15.2)**.
• Where necessary, mask the area surrounding the repair to prevent abrasive damage to existing good paintwork.
• If paint is to be sanded, ensure that it has fully cured before sanding commences. If the paint has not fully cured, sanding will leave tracks in the surface, and is also likely to clog the abrasive paper.
• Do not carry out any sanding on a colour coat which is to have a clear lacquer coat sprayed on top. If the colour coat is sanded, the colour tint will be distorted in the sanded area, causing a blemish which will be visible through the lacquer coat.

Sanding by hand

The following points should be borne in mind when sanding by hand. Refer to Chapter 7 for details of abrasives.

• When sanding by hand, remove jewellery (rings, watches, etc) which could cause accidental damage to the finish.

• The sanding block should be moved in all directions in a random motion, rather than rubbing back-and-forth with a regular action. This will help to avoid grooves or a regular sanding scratch pattern in the sanded surface.

• There's no need to apply heavy pressure when sanding by hand – let the abrasive do the work. Excessive pressure will produce grooves and sanding scratches in the finish.

• Take care not to allow the abrasive paper to crease or tear during use, as this can cause ridges and deep scratches in the finish.

• Wet-sanding can be carried out by hand, but it produces large amounts of residue, and is undesirable for the reasons already mentioned.

Sanding using a power sander

Power sanding should be carried out dry, using a dust extraction system to remove the residues. Various different types of power sanding tools are available, and these are described in Chapter 6.

Bear in mind the following points when using a power tool for sanding work:

• Wear overalls, and ensure that no loose clothing, jewellery, hair, etc, is able to come into contact with the tool when it is operating.

• Power sanders should always be started and stopped away from the work; start the tool, then move the tool onto the work, lifting the tool off the work before switching off.

• Always aim to keep the abrasive pad as flat as possible in relation to the work; using a power sander at an angle can cause uneven and very rapid removal of material.

• Don't apply excessive pressure. Most power sanders will sand very effectively using just the weight of the tool itself without any additional pressure, particularly when using fine abrasives.

• Stop to inspect the work frequently; a power sander can remove material very quickly.

• On completion of sanding, remove any contaminated masking materials, and re-mask ready for painting.

Sanding a corroded surface

Any corrosion on a metal substrate must be completely removed by sanding before the application of filler or paint. The abrasive must be used on the panel surface in such a way as to completely remove all corrosion, without reducing the strength of the panel itself.

Using a power sander with a course abrasive is the preferred method of removing corrosion, but care must be taken not to sand away the metal itself **(see illustration 15.3)**.

Sanding body filler

Refer to Chapter 10.

Sanding a painted surface (chip or scratch repair)

When repairing a minor chip or scratch, sanding is best carried out by hand, using progressively finer grades of abrasive paper. Finish sanding using around 320-grade abrasive to remove sanding scratches and minor imperfections, giving a smooth texture. Gradually sand away the paint around the damage to develop an obvious 'ring' around the repair area. The ring should expose a wide band of the material at the base of the damage, and then successive equally wide bands of the various remaining paint layers **(see illustration 15.4)**. If the damage has not penetrated the primer, sanding need only be carried out as far as the depth of the chip or scratch; there's no need to sand back to bare substrate. The object is to develop a smooth, gradual 'ramp' between the material at the base of the damage, and the top surface of the existing good paintwork. This will allow the new layers of paint to be applied to the same thickness as the surrounding original layers, and will help to blend in the repair, giving the new paint a similar colour and texture to the surrounding finish.

Sanding primer

Sometimes, depending on the type of primer applied, and the quality of the primer finish, it may be necessary to sand primer to give a smooth, flat surface, and to provide a key for the application of colour coat. Sanding of primer should be carried out in accordance with the recommendations give on the paint technical data/application sheet. Generally, very fine (around 800-grade) abrasives are used for sanding primer.

Cleaning a sanded surface

After sanding has been completed, thorough cleaning is required to remove

15.3 Using a power sander to remove corrosion from a damaged panel

15.4 When sanding a painted surface, aim to expose a wide band of material at the base of the damage, followed by bands of the remaining paint layers

15

any surface contamination before spraying paint. Wherever possible dust extraction equipment should be used when sanding, and this will help to prevent a build-up of dust on the panel surfaces. Make sure that all dust is removed from areas such as panel joins, gaps between the bonnet and wings, door jambs, etc, ideally using a dry cloth; although it may be tempting to blow dust off using an air line, bear in mind that this will blow the dust into the atmosphere, and it will eventually settle somewhere else – this is not desirable in a body shop environment.

Once the majority of any dust has been removed, the remaining residue can be removed using panel wipe. Panel wipe should be applied using a clean lint-free cloth, and wiped off using a second clean cloth. When applying panel wipe to a cloth, it's advisable to pour the liquid from its container onto the cloth; don't be tempted to place the cloth over the container and tip the container up to wet the cloth, as particles from the cloth may then contaminate the rest of the liquid in the

15.5 When using panel wipe, pour the liquid from the container onto the cloth

container (note that it's possible to obtain cloths which are impregnated with panel wipe) **(see illustration 15.5)**. All panel surfaces surrounding the repair should be cleaned, except for those which will be completely masked off.

The final stage in the cleaning process is to remove any loose dust and dirt particles using a tack cloth directly before the spraying commences (refer to Chapter 7 *Cleaning materials* for details of using tack cloths).

De-nibbing

Nibs are normally due to individual particles of dust or dirt, or possibly small insects, which settle on the paint or lacquer surface during drying. De-nibbing involves very light sanding to remove the nibs. De-nibbing can be carried out on primer or top-coats.

If nibs occur in a colour coat over which clear lacquer is to be sprayed, with

many paint systems the best course of action is to spray the lacquer coat (which will in itself hide the nibs to an extent), and remove any blemishes from the cured lacquer, followed by compounding and polishing (always follow the paint manufacturer's recommendations regarding de-nibbing base coat/lacquer coat finishes). With some paint systems,

sanding the colour coat can ruin the finish because it will disturb the metallic particles in the paint, causing a visible blemish. If de-nibbing is carried out on the colour coat, it may be necessary to spray further colour coat over the de-nibbed area in order to blend in the blemish created by de-nibbing.

The paint manufacturer's paint technical data/application sheet may provide information on recommended de-nibbing techniques. Most finishes can be de-nibbed using a wet-sanding (ie, with water) technique before they are fully cured **(see illustration 15.6)**.

Very fine abrasive paper (eg, 1000- or 1500-grade), or an abrasive pad should be used for de-nibbing. If abrasive paper is used, use a small sanding block. The object is to sand the nib level with the surrounding finish, without affecting the surrounding finish. Use a very light sanding action, and where possible, use water to reduce the harshness of the abrasive.

Any light swirl marks left by the sanding action when de-nibbing can be removed when the finish is compounded and polished (see Chapter 16).

15.6 De-nibbing a lacquer coat by wet-sanding using fine abrasive paper

Flatting

If fresh paint is sprayed over existing paint (or lacquer), without first flatting the paint surface, the new paint will not adhere to the existing paint, and it's highly likely that the new paint will eventually flake off.

During flatting, a mild abrasive is used to 'scuff' the surface of the existing paint or lacquer coat, providing a key to enable the new paint to adhere.

The size of the area which needs to be flatted will depend on the repair being carried out, and the type of finish (refer to Chapter 17 for an example of a typical blend repair procedure). Often, if a blend repair is being carried out on a panel which is finished with a lacquer coat, the lacquer coat on the entire panel is flatted; the complete panel can then be sprayed with lacquer to aid blending. In some cases, surrounding panels may be flatted and lacquered as well.

Flatting is carried out by hand, using a suitable flatting paste, and a lint-free cloth, or an abrasive pad **(see illustration 15.7)**.

Flatting the area surrounding a blend repair

Before using flatting paste, it's a good idea to mask the immediate surrounding area (wide masking tape should be sufficient), and any relevant badges and trim to prevent damage

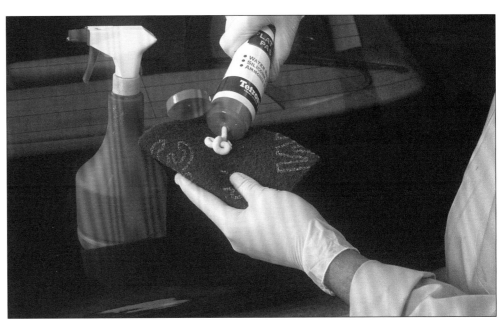

15.7 Applying flatting paste to an abrasive pad

from the gritty flatting paste. Don't mask ready for spraying at this stage, as the masking tape and paper will be contaminated during the flatting process.

Apply a little flatting paste to a clean lint-free cloth or an abrasive pad, and rub the paste into the finish. Refer to the manufacturer's recommendations, and use water if necessary to help to spread the paste. Water can be applied from a spray bottle as flatting progresses **(see illustration 15.8)**.

Take care not to apply excessive pressure when flatting; the aim is to key the surface without removing too much material, producing an even, matt finish.

Cleaning a flatted area

When flatting is complete, use fresh, clean water, and a clean, lint-free cloth to wash off the flatting paste and residue **(see illustration 15.9)**. Dry the panel thoroughly after washing.

Once the residue has been washed from the panel, remove any contaminated masking materials.

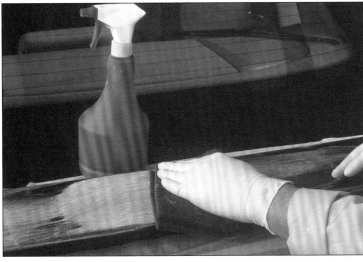

15.8 Rub the flatting paste into the finish, using water if necessary

15.9 Wash off flatting paste using clean water and a clean, lint-free cloth

15

Notes

Chapter 16
Wet-sanding, compounding and polishing the final finish

Contents

Introduction

The final stages in the refinishing process are the compounding and polishing of the finish to produce the final high-gloss finish. The degree of compounding and polishing carried out will depend to some extent on the type of finish, but when working with most 2-pack materials, compounding and final polishing will produce a brilliant lustre in the final finish **(see illustration 16.1)**.

The normal course of action when completing a refinishing job is to carry out any final de-nibbing of the finish, followed by machine compounding to remove any minor imperfections such as swirls marks and small blemishes, and then to use a wax polish to produce the final high-gloss finish.

Before considering any final compounding and polishing, it's essential to make sure that the paint is thoroughly dry. The paint technical data/application sheet will usually give details of the recommended curing time before the finish can be safely compounded.

All finishing abrasives work in the same way, and can be used by hand, or with the aid of a power tool. Ideally, most finishing work should be done using a power tool, fitted with an

appropriate pad for the work being done.

When carrying out final finishing work, cleanliness is absolutely vital. Even a single speck of grit or dirt can rapidly ruin the finish.

Compounding and polishing can be messy operations, and overalls and

gloves should be worn, not only to protect clothes, but also to prevent damage to the paintwork from belt buckles, rivets in jeans, etc. For the same reason, it's a good idea to remove any jewellery.

There are three basic techniques used to finish new paintwork; wet-

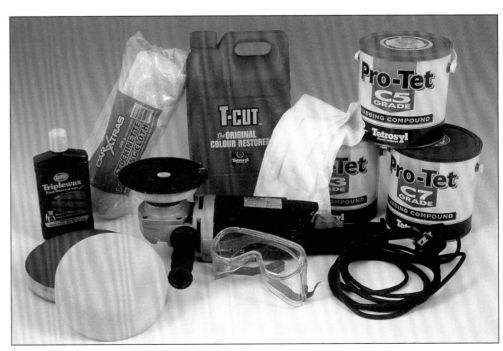

16.1 Typical materials and equipment used for finishing work

16

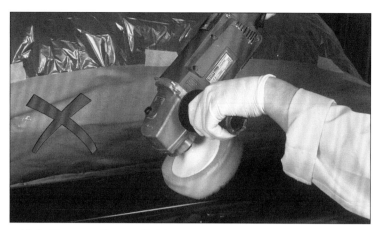

16.2 Do not tilt a polishing more than a few degrees . . .

16.3 . . . keep the pad as close as possible to horizontal

sanding (used for final de-nibbing – see Chapter 15), compounding and polishing. Before explaining these techniques in more detail, it's important to understand the effects of abrasives on paintwork.

Finishing abrasives

Abrasives for finishing new paint are available as papers, or compounding pastes and creams (see *Abrasives* in Chapter 7). These products contain very fine abrasives, much finer than those used for sanding filler and rubbing down prior to painting.

It's very important to use the finest abrasive possible for a particular job; abrasives work by removing paint, and it's desirable to keep the paint layer as thick as possible, to avoid exposing the primer, and to give maximum protection to the metal underneath.

Using an abrasive which is too coarse, or applying too much pressure, can mark the paint surface very quickly, and this type of damage can be difficult or impossible to remove, without the need for further refinishing.

Choosing the correct grade of abrasive is not an easy task, and is a skill which will come with experience. Most fine grade abrasives will have the same overall effect, the difference between them is the time taken to achieve an acceptable result. It's best to err on the side of caution and use a finer grade first; if it takes an unacceptably long time to have an effect, try a coarser grade.

Using polishing (buffing) machines

When using polishing machines, it's very easy to remove too much paint, which can have disastrous consequences.

Polishing machines require virtually no pressure when used for compounding and polishing work. The weight of the machine will usually be sufficient without applying any extra pressure. The tool should be allowed to 'float' over the panel surface. If too much pressure is applied, the heat generated can burn the paint layer, as well as removing too much paint.

When using a polishing machine, the pad should be kept as close as possible to horizontal. Never tilt the machine more than a few degrees, as this will increase the risk of marking the paint **(see illustrations 16.2 and 16.3)**. Rest the pad on the surface of the panel before starting the tool, and lift it clear before switching off.

When carrying out compounding and polishing work, make sure that a suitable foam or cloth (lambswool) pad is used, and make sure that the pad is securely fastened to the backing plate on the machine.

Always take care to keep machine electrical leads and/or air lines away from the vehicle bodywork to avoid scratches (looping the power lead or air line over a shoulder should keep it clear of the bodywork).

Wet-sanding

When working on finished paint, abrasive paper should always be used wet. Wet-sanding will only be necessary if there are serious defects in the paint finish, such as sags, runs, or dirt contamination. It's important to note that not all finishes are suitable for wet-sanding, and some types of finish may be permanently damaged if wet-sanding is carried out. Some finishes can be sanded shortly after they have cured, whilst others cannot be sanded for a considerable period of time. If in doubt, always consult the paint manufacturer's recommendations.

Usually, any nibs or dirt particles which need to be sanded out will be very small, which means that sanding is best carried out by hand, using paper wrapped around a small block (refer to *De-nibbing* in Chapter 15 for details) **(see illustration 16.4)**.

With most metallic and pearlescent finishes, any wet-sanding should only be carried out on the lacquer coat.

Wet-sanding should be carried out using very fine abrasive paper, ideally between 1000 and 1500 grade.

When wet-sanding, the aim should be to remove any nibs or blemishes, and to produce a perfectly smooth finish, which can then be compounded and polished.

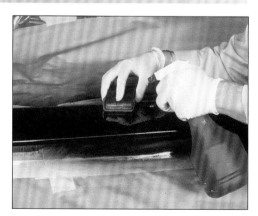

16.4 Wet-sanding a lacquer coat using fine abrasive paper wrapped round a block

Compounding

Compounding involves 'cutting' the finish with a compounding paste or cream. As with wet-sanding, it's wise to check the paint manufacturer's technical data/application sheet to make sure that the finish is compatible with compounding. Some finishes can be compounded shortly after they have cured, whilst others cannot be compounded for a considerable period of time.

Compounding is best used when there are no obvious major surface defects in the paint, or when any surface defects have been removed.

Like abrasive paper, compounding paste is available in various different grades. If a course compound is used to remove blemishes or 'orange peel', light scratches or 'swirls' (when using a polishing machine) will often be produced. This means that after using a coarse compound, the finish will need to be compounded using a finer compound to remove any scratches and swirls before final polishing.

Most modern compounds are water-based, and water can be used during compounding to aid spreading of the compound (follow the manufacturer's recommendations). Water can be applied using a spray bottle, but bear in mind that using water with a polishing machine can be messy!

To avoid possible contamination, it's a good idea to always refit the lid to tins of compound between applications.

Compounding with a polishing machine

When using a polishing machine for compounding, it's best to apply a few narrow strips of compounding paste to the panel at regular intervals, to cover a reasonable area (say a 600 mm square). The compounding pad can then be applied to each strip of paste to work it over the panel before moving on to the next strip. All the paste should be worked

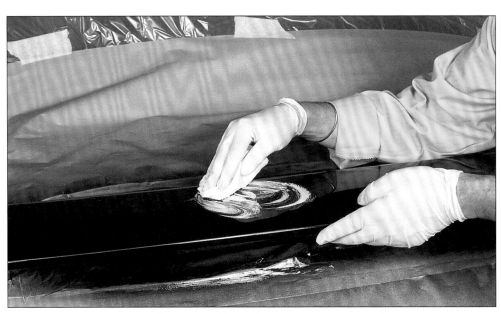

16.5 Compounding a lacquer coat by hand

into the panel without allowing the pad to become dry. Carry on compounding over this area until all the compound has been used, leaving a satisfactory compounded finish. Once the finish over the chosen area is satisfactory, repeat the process until all the relevant paintwork has been compounded.

When using a polishing machine to compound areas of paintwork at the edge of a panel, or next to trim, door handles, etc, it's sensible to reduce the speed of the tool. This will reduce the chances of burning the paint, and the possibility of the tool being deflected if the pad touches a piece of trim.

Make sure that the pad is cleaned regularly to avoid a build-up of paint; this is particularly important when using a cloth (lambswool) pad.

When working in very confined spaces, it's safer to apply compounding paste by hand, using a damp (not wet) cloth.

Compounding by hand

There's much debate about how compounding should be carried out by

hand. Some professionals prefer to use a straight-line to-and-fro rubbing action, whilst others prefer to work the compound with a random circular action. In theory, there should be less risk of scratching or gouging the surface using a circular action, although it's possible to make mistakes whichever method is used **(see illustration 16.5)**.

If compounding is being carried out by hand, always make sure that the cloths used are clean. Cloths should also be lint-free, and should have an open weave. An open weave is desirable because it will allow the paint removed, and the used compound, to be absorbed into the cloth as work progresses. If a closed weave cloth is used, material will tend to build up on the surface of the cloth, which can mark the surface of the paint. The cloth should be rinsed frequently to remove paint and used compound. Take care not to put a cloth down in an area where there may be dirt, and if a cloth is dropped on the floor, discard it and use a new one.

Polishing

Even if only a spot or panel repair has been carried out, it's advisable to polish the whole vehicle in order to blend in the repaired area. If only a small area is polished, it will be

obvious, and will draw attention to the repair.

Before finally polishing the vehicle, the vehicle should be thoroughly washed using detergent and water to

remove all of the residues left from compounding, as well as any accumulated dirt and dust. **Do not** use silicone or wax-based car wash additives.

The aim of polishing should be to produce a final even high-gloss finish. From the potential future refinishing point of view, polishes containing silicone should be avoided. Silicone polishes may produce an excellent gloss, but they are extremely difficult to remove, and will contaminate the painted surfaces, which prevents new paint from adhering. If possible, ordinary wax polishes should be used; they may prove more awkward to use, but the end result should be just as good as that obtained with silicone polish **(see illustration 16.6)**.

Always carry out final polishing by hand, and follow the guidelines given by the polish manufacturer. Always use clean, dry cloths, and use separate cloths for applying the polish, and buffing it off.

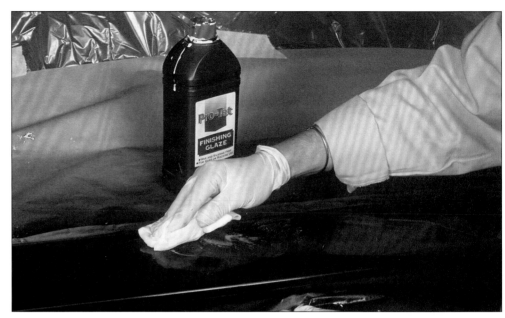

16.6 Carrying out final polishing

Chapter 17
Typical repair/refinishing procedures

Contents

Introduction

This Chapter draws on all the information given in the preceding Chapters to provide examples of two typical repair/refinishing procedures which are likely to be encountered frequently in the body shop.

The examples given in this Chapter should be studied after reading the preceding Chapters, as they are intended to show how the previously-explained theory and procedures are put to use. References are given to the relevant Chapters, where each step is explained in more detail.

Repairing and refinishing a scratched panel

This procedure assumes a minor scratch, where no filling is required.

1 Thoroughly wash the vehicle outside the body shop (see Chapter 9).
• Wash the vehicle to remove all obvious road dirt, tar and dust.
• Thoroughly dry the vehicle.

2 Assess the damage.
• Assess the damage, and decide on the most suitable procedure for carrying out the repair.
• Decide on the extent of the blending operation required.
• Assess the type and quantity of materials necessary to complete the repair, and make sure that all the necessary materials and equipment will be available when required.

3 Use panel wipe to clean the repair area.
• Panel wipe is used to thoroughly degrease the panel in order to prevent any contaminants from being driven into the repair area during sanding.
• Wipe off panel wipe using a clean, dry cloth.

17

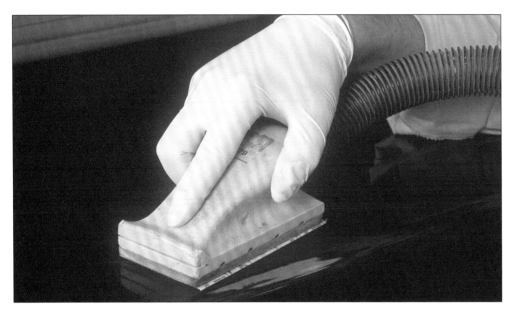

17.1 Sand the damaged area of the panel

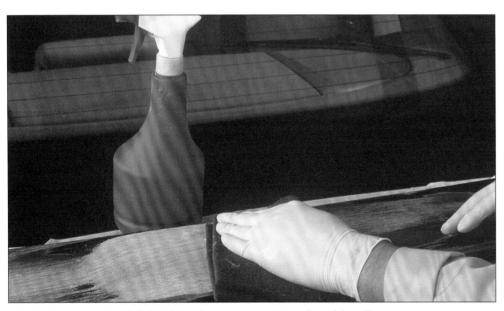

17.2 Flat the lacquer coat to allow blending

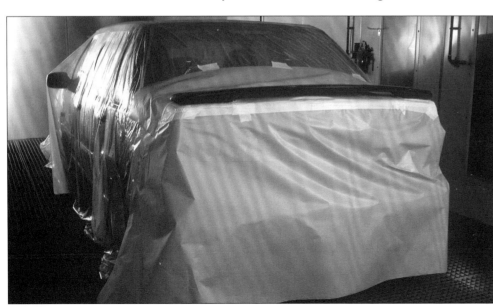

17.3 Carry out masking as required

4 Sand the damaged area of the panel (see Chapter 15).
• Depending on the degree of damage, sand the affected area by hand, or using a power sander. Sanding by hand should be sufficient for all but the most serious scratch damage **(see illustration 17.1)**.
• Decide on the most appropriate grade of abrasive paper, then sand to remove the scratch, and to allow blending with the surrounding paintwork.
• Where necessary, use progressively finer abrasive as sanding progresses to give a smooth, scratch-free surface for priming.

5 Use panel wipe to remove the sanding dust.
• Ensure that all sanding debris is removed from the repair area and surrounding panels.
• Wipe off panel wipe using a clean, dry cloth.

6 If the paint finish has a lacquer coat, flat the lacquer area surrounding the repair to allow blending (see Chapter 15).
• Use masking tape to protect the immediately surrounding paintwork and any badges and trim from the flatting paste.
• Use a suitable cloth, or an abrasive pad, to apply the flatting paste, and flat an area of lacquer large enough to allow blending when spraying the final lacquer coat over the repair **(see illustration 17.2)**.
• When flatting is complete, wash off all the deposits using clean, fresh water and a cloth.
• Remove any masking used to protect against the flatting paste.
• Use panel wipe (water-based) to degrease and clean the repair area. Wipe off the panel wipe using a clean, dry cloth.

7 Carry out masking as required (see Chapter 11).
• Mask the required area, leaving a sufficient area un-masked to allow for blending.
• Mask the remainder of the vehicle using a suitable plastic sheet **(see illustration 17.3)**.
• Degrease the repair area using panel wipe on completion of masking. Wipe off the panel wipe using a clean, dry cloth.

8 Tack-off the repair area using a tack cloth.

• Tack-off to remove any small dust and dirt particles **(see illustration 17.4)**.

9a If the panel has been sanded down to expose bare metal, spray etch primer over the affected area (see Chapter 13).

• If the original primer has not been rubbed through, there is no need to apply etch primer.

• Mix up the required quantity of etch primer in accordance with the manufacturer's recommendations.

• Ensure that the spray gun set up is correct (refer to the paint technical data/application sheet).

• Where applicable, thoroughly clean the spray gun before use.

• Spray the etch primer and then dry as recommended by the paint manufacturer.

• Thoroughly clean the spray gun after use.

9b If the panel has been sanded down to expose bare plastic, where necessary spray adhesion promoter over the affected area.

• Some plastics may require treating with an adhesion promoter to enable primer to adhere satisfactorily.

• Spray the adhesion promoter and then dry as recommended by the manufacturer.

10 Spray (high-build) primer over the repair area (see Chapter 13).

• Mix up the required quantity of primer in accordance with the manufacturer's recommendations.

• Where applicable, thoroughly clean the spray gun before use.

• Ensure that the spray gun set up is correct (refer to the paint technical data/application sheet).

• Use a tack cloth to remove any fine particles of dust and dirt just prior to spraying.

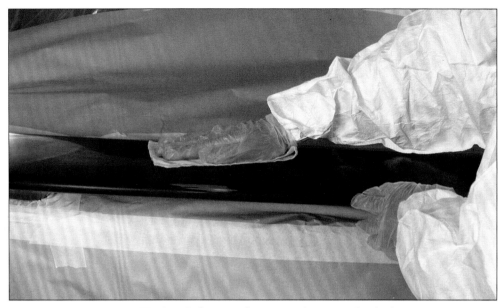

17.4 Tack-off the repair area using a tack cloth

• Spray primer over the required area, and dry as recommended by the paint manufacturer **(see illustration 17.5)**. If necessary, carry out light sanding of the primer.

• Thoroughly clean the spray gun after use.

11 Use panel wipe to clean the repair area.

• Clean the primed panel to remove any dirt and grease before spraying the colour coat.

• Wipe off panel wipe using a clean, dry cloth.

12 Spray the colour coat (see Chapter 13).

• Determine the required colour match, then mix up the required quantity of colour in accordance with the paint manufacturer's recommendations.

• Where applicable, thoroughly clean the spray gun before use.

• Ensure that the spray gun set up is correct (refer to the paint technical data/application sheet).

• Use a tack cloth to remove any fine particles of dust and dirt just prior to spraying.

• Spray colour coat over the required area to blend in with the surrounding paintwork, and dry as recommended by the paint manufacturer **(see illustration 17.6)**.

• Thoroughly clean the spray gun after use.

• Where the paint system allows, carry out any necessary de-nibbing.

13 If a clear lacquer coat is required, spray the lacquer coat (see Chapter 13).

• Check on the recommended time allowed between spraying colour coat and spraying lacquer, and do not exceed this time.

17.5 Spray high-build primer over the repair area

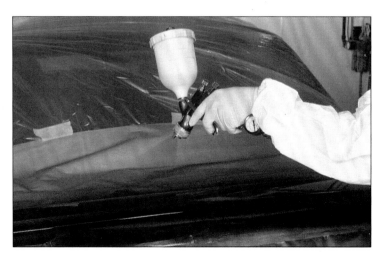

17.6 Spray the colour coat

17

17.7 Carry out any required de-nibbing

17.8 Compound the finish

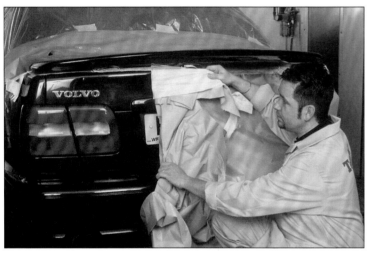

17.9 Remove the masking materials

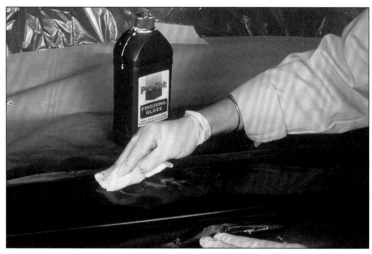

17.10 Wax the finish using non-silicone wax

• Mix up the required quantity of lacquer in accordance with the paint manufacturer's recommendations.
• Where applicable, thoroughly clean the spray gun before use.
• Ensure that the spray gun set up is correct (refer to the paint technical data/application sheet).
• Use a tack cloth to remove any fine particles of dust and dirt just prior to spraying.
• Spray lacquer over the required area to blend in with the surrounding

lacquer, and dry as recommended by the manufacturer.
• Thoroughly clean the spray gun after use.

14 Carry out any required de-nibbing (see Chapter 15).
• If necessary, de-nib the final finish by hand, using a block and very fine abrasive paper **(see illustration 17.7)**.

15 Compound the finish (see Chapter 16).
• Use suitable compounding cream and

a power polisher to compound the finish **(see illustration 17.8)**. Ensure that any marks left by de-nibbing are removed.

16 Remove the masking materials.
• Remove and discard all the masking materials used **(see illustration 17.9)**.

17 Polish the finish using non-silicone wax (see Chapter 16).
• If desired, a cleaning cream can be used before waxing.
• Ideally, the entire vehicle should be waxed **(see illustration 17.10)**.

Fitting and spraying a new panel

This procedure uses the renewal of a bolt-on front wing as an example.

1a If the new panel has not been primed, prepare the panel and spray primer as required.
• Panels will normally be supplied

primed, ready for application of colour.
• Repair any dents or scratches, prime complete panel, and if necessary sand finish ready for application of colour.

1b If the panel has been supplied primed, check for any damage and rectify as necessary.
• Repair any dents or scratches, and sand finish ready for application of colour.

• Prime complete panel if necessary (some refinishers may choose to do this as a matter of course).

2 Use panel wipe to clean the panel.
• Clean the primed panel to remove any dirt and grease before spraying the colour coat.
• Wipe off panel wipe using a clean, dry cloth.

3 Where necessary, apply underseal and stone chip protection to the panel.
• Where necessary, spray appropriate underseal on the vulnerable areas of the panel; eg, on the underside of a wing panel.
• Where necessary, spray stone chip protection on the lower exposed surfaces of the panel. Aim to replicate the manufacturer's finish; eg, some vehicles have stone chip protection applied to the lower edges of the wing panels and doors (colour coat can be sprayed over the top of stone chip protection).

4 Spray colour coat around the edges of the panel (see Chapter 13).
• The object of this stage of the procedure is to apply paint to the areas of the panel which will be obscured or difficult to reach, due to the panel profile, once the panel is fitted to the vehicle.
• Determine the required colour match, then mix up the required quantity of colour in accordance with the paint manufacturer's recommendations.
• Where applicable, thoroughly clean the spray gun before use.
• Ensure that the spray gun set up is correct (refer to the paint technical data/application sheet).
• Use a tack cloth to remove any fine particles of dust and dirt just prior to spraying.
• With the panel off the vehicle, spray colour coat around the edges of the new panel to allow blending once the new panel is fitted to the vehicle.
• Dry the panel as recommended by the paint manufacturer.
• Thoroughly clean the spray gun after use.

5 If the vehicle paint finish has a lacquer coat, flat the lacquer area surrounding the new panel to allow blending (see Chapter 15).
• Use masking tape to protect the

immediately surrounding paintwork and any badges and trim from the flatting paste.
• Use a suitable cloth, or an abrasive pad, to apply the flatting paste, and flat an area of lacquer large enough to allow blending when spraying the final lacquer coat over the repair; eg, if a new front wing is being fitted, it may be desirable to flat the lacquer on the whole of the adjoining door to allow adequate blending.
• When flatting is complete, wash off all the deposits using clean, fresh water and a cloth.
• Remove any masking used to protect against the flatting paste.
• Use panel wipe (water-based) to degrease and clean the repair area. Wipe off the panel wipe using a clean, dry cloth.

6 Fit the new panel to the vehicle.
• Where necessary, apply suitable sealant along panel joints.

7 Carry out masking as required (see Chapter 11).
• Mask the required area, leaving a sufficient area un-masked to allow for blending.
• Mask the remainder of the vehicle using a suitable plastic sheet).
• Degrease the repair area using panel wipe on completion of masking. Wipe off the panel wipe using a clean, dry cloth.

8 Spray colour coat over the whole of the new panel (see Chapter 13).
• Use a tack cloth to remove any fine

particles of dust and dirt just prior to spraying.
• Spray colour coat over the required area to blend in with the surrounding paintwork, and dry as recommended by the paint manufacturer **(see illustration 17.11)**.
• Thoroughly clean the spray gun after use.
• Where the paint system allows, carry out any necessary de-nibbing.

9 If a clear lacquer coat is required, spray the lacquer coat (see Chapter 13).
• Check on the recommended time allowed between spraying colour coat and spraying lacquer, and do not exceed this time.
• Mix up the required quantity of lacquer in accordance with the paint manufacturer's recommendations.
• Where applicable, thoroughly clean the spray gun before use.
• Ensure that the spray gun set up is correct (refer to the paint technical data/application sheet).
• Use a tack cloth to remove any fine particles of dust and dirt just prior to spraying.
• Spray lacquer over the required area to blend in with the surrounding lacquer, and dry as recommended by the manufacturer.
• Thoroughly clean the spray gun after use.

10 Proceed as described previously in steps 14 to 17 of the procedure given for repairing and refinishing a scratched panel.

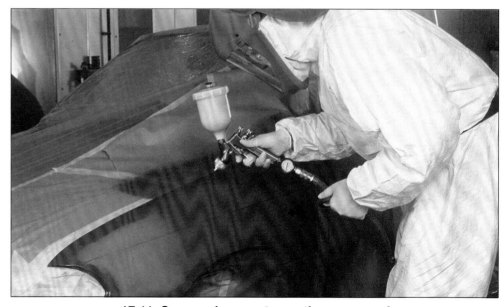

17.11 Spray colour coat over the new panel

Notes

Chapter 18
Fault diagnosis

Introduction

To avoid problems, ensure that the paint is mixed in accordance with the manufacturer's recommendations, and ensure that the paint manufacturer's recommended spray gun set-up data is observed.

This Chapter does not aim to provide comprehensive information on all the possible faults which may be encountered during refinishing work, but aims to deal with the most common faults which are likely to be visible in the final finish, particularly those likely to be encountered by inexperienced sprayers.

The recommendations appearing in this table apply primarily to modern 2-pack paints, but much of the information applies equally to cellulose-based paints, etc.

Fault diagnosis

Acid and alkali spotting

Appearance
Spotty discoloration of the surface (different pigments react differently when exposed to acids or alkalis)

Cause
Chemical change of pigments due to atmospheric contamination, in the presence of moisture
Battery acid spills
Brake/hydraulic fluid spills
Acid rain (near industrial areas)

Prevention
Avoid contaminated atmosphere around finish
If finished surface is contaminated, flush the surface immediately with cool water and detergent

Remedy
Wash with detergent and water, followed by diluted vinegar
Sand and refinish
If contamination has reached the substrate or sub-coating, sand spot down to metal before refinishing

Bleaching or peroxide bleaching

Appearance
Discolouring of paint surface corresponding to areas of body filler in substrate

Cause
Excess quantities of hardener (peroxide) used in filler

Prevention
Take care to calculate and measure hardener quantities accurately
Observe recommended working temperature of filler
When using filler in cold ambient temperature, raise ambient temperature Do not use extra hardener to compensate

Remedy
Totally remove affected paint and underlying filler, and start repair process again

Bleeding

Appearance
Discoloration of the surface of the refinish colour (halo, or complete colour change)

Cause
Solvent from refinishing material dissolves original finish, releasing dye which comes to the surface
Usually reds and maroons
Painting white over red colour

Prevention
Apply 2-pack high-build primer over any areas which it suspected may bleed, before spraying new colour

Remedy
Either:
• Remove all colour coats, and re-coat
Or:
• Allow surface to cure, then re-coat

Blistering

Appearance
Small swollen areas, similar to water blister on human skin
Lack of gloss in small blisters
Broken-edged craters if blisters have burst

Cause
Corrosion under surface
Paint applied over oil or grease
Moisture in spray gun lines
Trapped solvents in paint layer
Prolonged or repeated exposure to high humidity
Moisture absorbed in body filler
Inadequate cleaning of panel surface

Prevention
Thoroughly clean metal and treat against corrosion
Frequently check spray gun air line for water
Ensure paint thinner used is suitable for ambient temperature
Allow sufficient drying/flash-off times between coatings

Remedy
Sand and refinish blistered areas

Blooming and Blushing (acrylics and lacquer)

Appearance	Cause	Prevention	Remedy
Milky looking finish Haze or mist on surface	Incorrect thinner used in high humidity (associated with cellulose paints) Condensation on original finish Incorrect thinners used in low ambient temperature (associated with cellulose paints) Paint sprayed at correct temperature, then left in lower ambient temperature – paint then absorbs moisture as it cures (associated with flat panel surfaces) Excess activator in paint (usually due to low ambient temperature)	Ensure ambient temperature is not too cold Keep paint and surface to be sprayed at ambient temperature Use good quality 'anti-bloom' thinner (cellulose paints) Ensure correct quantity of activator is used	Either: • Add thinner/activator and re-spray Or: • Sand and refinish • Polish paint surface (cellulose paints)

Chalking

Appearance	Cause	Prevention	Remedy
Lack of gloss Powdery surface	Natural weathering of paint film Use of strong traffic film removers Use of poor quality thinner (cellulose paints) Natural breakdown of main tinter (usually due to age or prolonged strong sunlight)	Mix colour coats thoroughly Use good quality thinner (cellulose paints)	Sand to remove soft surface material, then clean and refinish (cellulose paints) Use paint restorer/polishing compound Sand and refinish in severe cases

Checking, crazing and cracking

Appearance	Cause	Prevention	Remedy
Crowsfoot separation (checking) Appearance similar to shattered glass (crazing) Irregular separation (cracking)	Insufficient drying/flash-off times between coatings Repeated extreme temperature variations Excessively heavy coats Paint constituents not thoroughly mixed Mixing of incompatible paint constituents Re-coating a previously checked finish Thinner attacking the surface of a cured acrylic lacquer (crazing) Solvents or petrol penetrating paint film (especially thermo-plastic acrylics)	Allow sufficient drying/flash-off times between coatings Avoid extreme temperature changes (hot climates) Spray even coats, avoiding excess, particularly with lacquers Mix all paint constituents thoroughly Use appropriate, good quality thinner and activator Don't re-coat over a checked finish	Remove damaged paint layer(s) and refinish

Dirt in finish

Appearance	Cause	Prevention	Remedy
Foreign particles embedded in paint film	Poor cleaning, drying and tacking-off of surface to be sprayed Faulty spray gun air cleaner filter Dirty working area Faulty or dirty spray booth air inlet filters Dirty spray gun	Blow out all cracks and body joints using air line Use panel wipe and tack cloth on surface before spraying Ensure all equipment is clean Ensure spray area is clean Renew spray booth air inlet filters Strain any foreign matter from paint Keep all containers closed when not in use to prevent contamination	Rub finish with polishing compound If dirt is deep in finish, sand and compound. Metallic finishes may show mottling after sanding and compounding, and will require additional colour coats

Fisheyes and poor wetting ('sissing' or silicone marks)

Appearance	Cause	Prevention	Remedy
Separation of the wet paint film Previous finish can be seen in spots Craters (smooth) Dishes (sometimes clustered, or individual)	Poor cleaning of surface Spraying over finishes which contain silicone Silicone polishes Use of space heaters (paraffin and diesel) Recently-valeted vehicle Finger prints (not wearing latex gloves) Dried soap Washer jet fluid	Use panel wipe to remove all waxes, oils and silicone from surface	Remove paint whilst still wet (wash immediately) Allow paint to cure, then sand and refinish Use 'anti-sissing' additive

Lifting or reacting

Appearance	Cause	Prevention	Remedy
Lifting and swelling of the wet paint film Peeling when the surface is dry Crocodile skin	Insufficient drying/flash-off times between coatings Sandwiching base coat between two layers of acrylic or lacquer Spraying onto poorly cleaned surface	Clean surfaces thoroughly Allow sufficient drying/flash-off times between coatings	Isolate whole surrounding area, then remove paint, and refinish

Mottling or striping

Appearance	Cause	Prevention	Remedy
Streaks in base coat – with metallic finishes	Excessive wetting of some areas Inconsistent film thickness Poor spraying technique Poor spray pattern Incorrect spray gun set-up	Avoid excessive wetting or heavy film build-up in localised areas Ensure correct thinner is used Do not use excessive thinner Ensure correct spraying technique Ensure correct spray gun set-up	If colour is freshly applied, apply a drop coat. Avoid excessive thinner In extreme cases, if colour has dried, flat down and apply additional colour coat

Orange peel

Appearance
Finish resembles skin of an orange
Finish resembles small ball-pein hammer dents in paint

Cause
Insufficient thinning of paint
Incorrect thinner used
Poor flow from spray gun
Incorrect spay gun pressure
Surface drying too fast

Prevention
Check set-up of spray gun
Use correct thinner and activator
Check paint manufacturer's recommended viscosity and spraying/drying temperature

Remedy
Either:
• Base coat: rub surface with mild polishing compound
• Lacquer: sand or use flatting compound
Or:
• Sand and refinish

Peeling or de-laminating

Appearance
Separation of paint film from surface underneath (from primers up to lacquers)

Cause
Poor surface preparation
Incompatibility between paint types
Contamination of underlying surface
Etch primer not used on galvanised metal surfaces
Inadequate keying of surface
Surface too hot or too cold when sprayed
Incorrect primer process
Paint film applied too thickly
Final base coat applied far too lightly (lacquer adheres to final base coat and peels)
Too much time allowed between base coat and lacquer

Prevention
Thoroughly clean and prepare surface
Use appropriate primer
Ensure materials used are compatible with each other and with original finish

Remedy
Remove all peeling paint, prepare surface correctly and refinish

Pitting or cratering

Appearance
Small craters
Appearance similar to dry spray or overspray

Cause
Refer to *Blistering* (except that blisters have broken)

Prevention
Refer to *Blistering*

Remedy
Refer to *Blistering*

Water spotting

Appearance
Dulling of gloss in spots
Mass of spots which appear as a large distortion of the paint film

Cause
Spots of water drying on a finish which is not thoroughly dry
Washing finish in bright sunlight

Prevention
Don't allow water or rain to contact a newly painted surface
Don't allow water to dry on a new finish
Avoid strong sunlight when washing finish

Remedy
Flat and use polishing compound
Extreme cases: Sand and refinish

Wrinkling

Appearance
Puckering of paint surface
Prune skin effect
Loss of gloss as paint dries (minute wrinkling not visible to the naked eye)

Cause
Excessive thinners in base coat
Excessive paint film thickness
Solvents trapped in surface layer during drying (particularly synthetic finish)
Fresh paint film exposed to heat too soon (particularly synthetic finish)

Prevention
Use recommended type and quantity of thinner and activator
Check spray gun set-up
Allow sufficient flash-off time before forced drying

Remedy
Sand to break open top surface, then allow paint to dry (synthetic paints).
When paint has dried, sand and refinish (sealing with a primer may be needed to cover damaged area)

18

Runs

Appearance	Cause	Prevention	Remedy
Running of wet paint film in rivulets Mass slippage of entire paint film Wavy lines on vertical surfaces	Excess thinner and activator with insufficient air pressure when spraying Spraying onto cold surface	Check paint viscosity Check set-up of spray gun Don't spray onto cold surface	Severe cases: Remove paint and refinish Minor runs: Flat surface and use polishing compound

Sags

Appearance	Cause	Prevention	Remedy
Partial slipping of paint in curtains, caused by a paint film which is too heavy to support itself	Insufficient drying/flash-off times between coatings Spray gun air pressure too low Spray gun held too close to panel Incorrect spray gun set-up	Use recommended type and quantity of thinner and activator (eg, fast or slow activator as appropriate) Allow sufficient drying/flash-off times between coatings Check spray gun set-up Keep spray gun at correct distance from panel	Sand and refinish

Corrosion under finish

Appearance	Cause	Prevention	Remedy
Peeling or blistering Raised surface spots	Poor preparation of metal Broken paint film allowing moisture to creep under surrounding finish Water in spray gun air lines (during initial priming)	Ensure metal is correctly prepared and primed (using etch primer) Locate any sources of moisture and rectify When refitting trim, take care not to break the paint film, or to allow dissimilar metals to come into contact (this can cause electrolysis which may cause corrosion and/or a loss of adhesion with the paint film)	Remove any sources of moisture Sand down to bare metal, treat, prime and refinish as necessary

Glossary of terms

Achromatic – 'Neutral' colours; eg, whites, greys, beiges

Acrylic – A paint in which an acrylic-based **binder** is used. Usually dries shiny; can be used with or without clear-coat.

Activator – A component of filler or 2-pack paint which reacts chemically with another component to form a hard finish.

Back masking – A masking technique where rolled masking tape or foam tape is used to avoid hard edges when spraying up to a masked line.

Base coat – A solid colour, pearlescent or metallic colour coat over which a clear coat must be sprayed.

Base paint – See **Tinter**.

Binder – A constituent of paint which is used to hold the pigments together, and provide the medium for the pigments to flow and bond to a surface.

Binding agent – See **Binder**.

Cataphoretic dipping – An electrical process used in a vehicle factory-finishing process, in which body panels are submerged in a tank of paint/electrolyte solution in order to coat them evenly with primer.

Catalyst – See **Activator**.

Cathodic dipping – See **Cataphoretic dipping**.

Cellulose – A paint in which a cellulose-based **binder** is used.

Chromatic – Clearly-defined colours; eg, reds and greens

Clear-coat – A transparent top-coat sprayed over the top of a colour coat.

Colour coat – A coloured paint layer sprayed over the top of primer to give a vehicle its colour.

Compounding – Compounding involves 'cutting' the finish with a compounding paste or cream to remove any minor imperfections in the finish before final polishing.

Cross coating – See **Drop coating**.

De-nibbing – Light sanding to remove particles of dust or dirt, or possibly small insects, which settle on the paint or lacquer surface during drying.

Drop coating – A spraying method used to cover 'striping' in a metallic colour coat. For a drop coat, the air pressure is lowered, and the panel is sprayed in the opposite direction to the previous passes. This method should not be used on highly visible panel areas.

Electrophoresis/ Electrophoretic dipping – See **Cataphoretic dipping**.

Electrostatic spraying – A paint spraying process where the paint particles are electrostatically-charged, and instead of a conventional spray gun, special jets are used to spray the paint onto the electrostatically-charged body.

Enamel – A paint which dries due to a chemical reaction between two or more elements.

Etch primer – The purpose of an etch primer is to replicate the galvanising process used to protect vehicle panels against corrosion. Etch primers contain an acid which etches bare metal, ensuring that there is a very strong bond between the primer and the panel surface.

Extender – See **High-build primer**.

Filler – A material used to fill large imperfections in the surface of a panel, which can be sanded level with the surrounding panel surfaces, to provide a smooth surface ready for priming.

Flash-off – The 'flash-off time' is the recommended time for which a coat of paint must be left to air dry after spraying, to allow most of the volatile solvent material in the paint to evaporate.

Flatting – A process where a mild abrasive is used to 'scuff' the surface of the existing paint (or lacquer) coat, providing a key to enable new paint (or lacquer) to adhere.

Galvanising – Galvanising involves coating a panel with a thin layer of zinc to provide corrosion protection.

Hard edge – A hard edge is produced when paint is sprayed directly up to an edge such as a piece of trim, or masking tape. The build-up of new paint film produces a step between the new paint and the surrounding original finish, which is highly visible.

Hardener – See **Activator**.

High-build primer – A **primer** paint which is sprayed before colour coat is applied, and has three main functions; to provide a relatively thick coating which will fill any small imperfections; to provide an element of stone chip resistance; and to provide a coating which can be sanded to give a smooth, sound base on to which colour coat can be sprayed.

HVLP – High Volume Low Pressure. A method of spraying paint, which uses a low air pressure, and a high volume of paint. This spraying method reduces the level of **overspray**, and reduces **VOC** emissions.

Lacquer – A paint which dries through solvent evaporation or by oxidation of the binder. A term also used to describe a **clear-coat**.

Metamerism – A phenomenon whereby two samples of a colour look the same under a particular colour of light, but are in fact made up from different mixtures of pigments. When the two samples are viewed under a different light source, they appear to be different colours.

Overspray – Particles of paint which settle and dry on areas surrounding the repair area during spraying.

Panel wipe – A solvent-based cleaning fluid which is used to remove grease and contamination from panels during the refinishing process.

Peroxide – A strong oxidising agent which is used as a hardening agent in body fillers.

Phosphatising – A process in which a bare vehicle body shell is submerged in a bath containing a solution of various phosphate salts. Crystalline metal phosphates are deposited on the panels to give corrosion protection, and to provide a good base to enable paint to adhere.

Pigment – Very fine particles of solid material, which are used to give a paint its colour and 'body'.

Polyester – A paint in which an polyester-based **binder** is used. Usually dries matt and finished with a clear-coat.

Primer – A paint of neutral colour which is designed to provide a coating which will fill any small imperfections (eg, minor scratches and sanding marks) in the finish underneath, and to provide a coating which can be sanded to give a smooth, sound base on to which colour coat can be sprayed.

Primer filler – See **High-build primer**.

Resin – A substance which is neither volatile, nor solid; eg, the **binder** in a paint.

Roll masking – See **Back masking**.

Solid colour – A paint in which only solid colour pigments are used; ie, a paint without metallic or pearlescent pigments. Solid colour **base coats** are available, which give a matt finish, and require a clear-coat to be sprayed over the top.

Solvent – A Volatile Organic Compound (**VOC**), such as acetone, petroleum products, butyl acetate, etc.

Solvent-based paint – A paint which contain solvents and thinners consisting of Volatile Organic Compounds (**VOC**s), such as acetone, petroleum products, and butyl acetate.

Solvent-borne paint – See **Solvent-based paint**.

Stopper – A low density body filler.

Substrate – A material to which paint is applied; eg, galvanised steel, plastic, aluminium, etc.

Surfacer – See **High-build primer**.

Thinner – A solvent which is added to paint to reduce its viscosity.

Tinter – A coloured base paint. To mix a specific paint colour, a number of tinters are mixed in the proportions specified in the paint manufacturer's paint formulation.

Top-coat – The final layer of paint to be sprayed. Usually either a solid colour coat, or a clear lacquer coat.

VOC – Volatile Organic Compound. Chemical substances which rise into the atmosphere and react with nitrous oxides to produce ozone. The most significant source of VOCs is chemical solvents.

Water-based paint – A paint in which water forms the main constituent of the solvent and thinner (the paint still contains some solvent).

Water-borne paint – See **Water-based paint**.

Wet-on-wet – The application of a paint layer on top of an existing paint layer before the existing paint layer is fully dry.

Index